THE BRIDPORT

POETRY, SHORT STORIES

CW00735886

JUDGES
Raymond Antrobus • Poetry
Robert McCrum • Short Stories and Flash Fiction

First published in 2021 by Redcliffe Press Ltd
81g Pembroke Road, Bristol BS8 3EA
e: info@redcliffepress.co.uk
www.redcliffepress.co.uk

Follow us on Twitter @RedcliffePress

Follow The Bridport Prize:
Follow us on Twitter and Instagram @BridportPrize

www.bridportprize.org.uk
www.facebook.com/bridportprize

ISBN 978-1-911408-86-4

British Library Cataloguing-in-Publication Data
A catalogue record for this book is available from the British Library

Typeset in 10.5pt Times

Typeset by Addison Print Ltd, Northampton
Printed by Hobbs the Printers Ltd, Totton

Contents

Poetry Report

This year's Bridport poetry prize was <u>the</u> toughest competition I have ever judged! Such a wide and impressive range of ideas, tones, forms (traditional and invented).

I enjoyed how playful and humorous many entries were. It's clear the pandemic (and the general sense of impending doom) hasn't stifled poetic imaginations. Poems had me chuckling, nodding my head, gasping (and in a few cases, actually standing up to applaud).

To read so many poems of this quality did more than inspire me, it assured me that poetry is continuing to be pushed and expanded and ideas of what a poem is (or can be) is still being explored and renewed.

I believe we've entered an age of cross-genre and interdisciplinary exploration; that some of the most compelling poets writing today are borrowing from other art forms, that some poems are part-poem, part-archival practise, part-essay, part-translation.

Poetry is more democratic this way. Its reputation as an elite endeavour is (rightfully) fading. If this weren't true, such a rich range of voices and styles would simply not be possible. I want to stress that I'm not just commentating on the winning poems, but an overall feeling that arose after reading <u>ALL</u> the shortlisted poems. But my assignment was to choose the poems that felt most striking, that lingered long after initial readings that had an image, a style, a voice, an energy with staying power.

I'm going to start with ten fantastic highly commended poems. All of them move towards aliveness. They sing and shake on the page in voices that feel unique and earned. I can't wait to hear more from these poets.

The deftly done sequence poem '76', is an Orwellian cautionary tale and an 'experiment in time' as the speaker calls it, an accomplished and fully realised voice.

'Jamaica Grapples with "Til Death Do Us Part"', a dramatic lyrical monologue in Patois that is shocking and stinging with its fresh mash up of language and sharp striking phrases like 'triangular rage' and 'pocketable for the sky.'

'We Real Spinsters' pays literary homage to some of the best poets and writers of recent centuries using Gwendolyn Brooke's 'We Real Cool', this poem feels like a chant, a roll call of names and deliciously compelling lyric sound, "We // Spare Rib // We // Women's Lib // We…".'

'Becoming Catwoman' is a poem that feels like a friend confiding in its readers, at once humorous and strikingly violent, but clever and subtle in its 'killing' final lines.

'A Hill In November' is a brilliant pastoral poem that is (very cleverly) anchored by the remembered image of 'whales here at dusk // on an allotment far from the ocean'. The premise itself is a fresh and subversive approach to the pastoral poem.

'Cradled' is powerful and tender. The language gets more minimal and leaves us, stung with the image – 'Cradled in silence // It was empty– // my womb.'.

'eating god for breakfast' is a wonky shape for such a precise poem, where language itself is digested and broken up. Here's the fleshy opening – 'we are at the kitchen table eating eggs, and god // i love sundays. i imagine keeping sunday so close to me // tattooed on my sternum, or across my knuckles, sun // day, in two easy halves.'.

In the poem, 'Fit for Work', a clever sonnet-y poem that subtly challenges every-day ableism using a familiar analogy about Stephen Hawking. 'He had a lot to say about the universe // And his mouth stopped working.' Yet it's in the final turn of the poem, the speaker asking its (abled bodied listener) to consider the value of the disabled body (and mind). I think it's a risky (deliberately imperfect) poem and one that would inspire thought and debate in any setting.

'When Two Men, All Pupil No Sclera' is a poem that witnesses the death of (another) unarmed Black man murdered in police violence (*Ahmaud Arbery*). The poem is lyrical reportage, it doesn't function to beautify the (already sensational) death, but, using visceral imagery like 'windows waiting for glass', it brings us closer to the human layer often missing in (dehumanising) journalism.

Finally, 'In Memoriam', a beautifully crafted poem about an unsentimental mother who 'doesn't see the point in monuments' yet, finds a (simultaneously private and public) way to sentimentalise the loss of a loved one (ironically) in print.

In 3rd place, the poem 'Bruised Fruit' opens with the unforgettable couplet,

'I travel as I live: among the hurt
and hurried, though not as breathless'

That opening is as memorable as many of our canonised poems. A masterful display of enjambments as the poem continues to breathlessly (and effortlessly) unfold. Without the couplet form and each full stop and comma, each image, question and proposition could easily overwhelm the reader (like the woman who can't catch her bracelets when they break away from her wrist). I can't resist the pun, but it is a muscular poem. Look at these active word choices – 'bends, breaks, leans, stretches, stands and swells', the poem does everything magical the body does.

In 2nd place the poem, 'Guidance Patrol', a powerfully rendered Ghazal that stayed with me, even as I cooked my dinner the night after I read it. The heightened drama perfectly suited to the heightened language.

'When the black van pulled over, my hand was in yours.

They thought I was your lover: my hand was in yours.'

The repeated line is haunting and beautiful. Such light touches are incredibly powerful, carefully handled. The danger is both immediate and historical. (Soldiers, war, crumbled remains, city and body.) The word 'faithful' is compounded with the divine, but also the belief of love itself. It's a kind of faithful balancing act, showing us in its preserving refrain, what it takes to love a person and a place (despite, despite).

In first place, 'Over the Tannoy', a poem that fed my sensibilities as a poet, family archivist, political commentator and emotional historian, a new kind of (immersive) found poem, a new way of speaking to and from a lineage, an ancestor, an intergenerational collaboration.

I don't just want to read poems like this, I want to read essays about poems like this, I want to see the cinema, the photography, the paintings that poems like this could inspire. I champion this work as a soulful language experiment, a form to be brought forward by more poets, to inspire more writers to delve into family archives. I say this knowing the privilege of having access to your history, of having an archive to explore, of having poet-ancestors, (blood and chosen). 'Over The Tannoy' works as a contrapuntal poem, a found poem, a letter poem, multiple forms and two voices happening at once.

Remarkable!

ROBERT McCRUM

Short Story Report

2021 is the second year in which this great international story prize has been conducted in the shadow of Covid-19. Once again, so many impressive tales have been conceived and written in the almost ideal creative conditions of solitude, solemnity and silence within an atmosphere of universal dread.

It's often said that fiction is a mirror, but I beg to disagree. Stories don't just reflect, they open windows. This year's entries will take the reader into many new worlds of life, love and loss. These may been provoked by lockdown, but they're about so much more than the pandemic. Far from reflecting the vicissitudes we've all endured, these stories draw inspiration from a timeless range of individual experience and the compelling dramas of everyday life. Sure, there are intermittent nods to intubation, the ICU and lateral flow tests. But what's more striking, to me, is the resilient way in which a global crisis has become absorbed into the context of quotidian reality. Perhaps there's less comedy, and more grief in these pages than hitherto, but in almost all other respects, these Bridport stories offer fine examples of a much-loved genre.

And what is that genre? It has become an indispensable lifeline, transistorized fiction for distracted and disrupted times: a contemporary means of self-expression inspired by those great artists of the story – Raymond Carver, Jennifer Egan, Deborah Eisenberg, Richard Ford, Thom Jones, Lorrie Moore, and Alice Munro, among many.

As an annual celebration of short-fiction, Bridport is proud to be a global prize, and the two daunting shortlists from which I've made my selection exemplify the international reach of the English literary tradition, with submissions from Canada, Scotland, Australia, the USA, Northern Ireland and the Home Counties. As a judge, I had no idea what to expect, but it was not really a surprise to find the recurring themes of love betrayed, identity in crisis and families divided.

The ten Highly Commended stories make a show-case for the range and ambition of the prize-entries as a collective. 'The Hall of Human Origins', an American story, is notable for its boldness, squarely set in the midst of the pandemic, with a marriage unravelling in an atmosphere of seething hysteria. There's a risk to such topicality, and 'The Sound of Summer', set in the Northern Ireland of the Troubles, demonstrates the dividends a story will get from hindsight. 'A Diamond in this Rhinestone World' is another American story set in a desert part of Texas, a wasted environment in which Jesus Christ and Dolly Parton compete for supremacy in the mind of Liz as she struggles to find love amid the desolation of the American south. 'The Leavetaking' is so short it's almost an exercise in flash fiction, but it demonstrates superbly the power of Less is More in an arresting break-up story. 'A Woman of Paris (1921)' is a highly entertaining historical fantasy, set in Twenties Hollywood, sustaining themes of gender and celebrity with scintillating dialogue.

Still in the USA (always a source of excellent short fiction), 'Gia's Midsummer Eve' unfolds an unforgettable suburban nightmare with calculated contemporary nods to *The Great Gatsby*, another risk, but one that almost comes off. 'The Entomologist's Pin' is an accomplished horror story, 'The Hot House' and 'The Arrival Fallacy' boldly play with comic material in Australia and Scotland, respectively. 'Mission Accomplished' is a gay, coming-of-age love-story set against the Iraq war. All of the above promise well for the future.

And so to my winning trio: the third prize, which goes to 'Looking for Light in the *Cingulate Cortex*', is a witty and ambitious literary satire about "the neuro-imaging of love". On my reading, this was pipped at the post by the winner of the second prize, 'A breath is a motion is the air rising is water flowing', a witty, and quite merciless, portrait of a gay couple in meltdown.

Within the agonised internal debate any judge of new fiction must endure, my overall winner is that joyous thing – the unanimous choice of my various reading selves. 'Manischewitz Night' captured my attention on first encounter, and no amount of re-reading shook my conviction that this is the real thing. Did I want to hear a new voice? Here, from the first line, is a woman with a scene to paint, a mood to capture, and something she has to get off her chest... Did I want character? Our narrator and her posse (Abby, Cameron, Kiva, Jen, and Thalia) are great personalities, six original and outrageous young women on the raz. The best company, cracking some great lines – too many to quote – on a freezing night in mid-winter Toronto.

So it's 'Manischewitz Night' that takes the Bridport Short Story prize summa cum laude; I, for one, will eagerly wait to see what its author writes next.

ROBERT McCRUM

Flash Fiction Report

In *Mothers, Fathers and Others*, her latest volume of essays, the distin-
guished American novelist Siri Hustvedt writes, of reading, that it's an
intimate encounter 'every person can have during a pandemic. No social
distance is required. In our current world of restricted movement, the
book is a geography where complete freedom remains possible.' By the
same token, the literary act of writing also remains unrestricted. And
when it comes to the upstart genre of 'flash fiction', readers and writers
alike still find themselves in an intoxicating world of instant gratification:
an extraordinary encounter, a memorable turning-point, or a stunning
revelation – that rare snapshot which says everything.

If a successful short-story is a star-turn, then flash fiction, like a ram-
bunctious sibling, is improv. on a stick. Nothing if not a show-off, the
flash fiction writer must be flash: nail it from the outset, take the reader
by the throat, and stop on a dime – a high-wire act that's not for the faint-
hearted.

Not every contribution to the shortlist for this demanding category had
quite the ice-cool mastery of their material I was looking for – that elusive
'voice' – but the following Highly Commended entries each make a
compelling claim on the reader: from the raw heart-break of 'Trauma
Light', and the jaunty 'Swim the Bay with Byron', to the insouciant heart-
lessness of 'New You', and the heart-felt confessional of 'Unsent'. In
'Present Perfect', 'people are hanged' becomes the macabre coda to this
chilling snapshot of a father-daughter relationship. Still, however, I was
looking....

Finally, it was the overall winner (whose title 'What to Watch' made its
own claim), whose seamless single paragraph fulfilled almost all my
criteria, and made me smile too. Here was a single page that was on-the-
money: responding to the challenge of a tricky genre, playing with the
conventions, and (with 'it's this one moment') delivering on time.
Nevertheless, it was chased down the final furlong by 'Pineapples', the
story I awarded second prize, a poignant terminal duologue from within
the ICU, and third prize 'The Value of Things,' a memorable and moving
meditation on 'last things'. Congratulations all round.

EMMA WALTON HAMILTON

Over the Tannoy

A conversation with my great-grandfather, a twentieth-century South Yorkshire coal miner and poet. His public domain letter is in the left column, my response is on the right. The combined lines form an additional poem, to be read across both columns.

I wish *I could read your Poems*
to inform the public *not just the horses*
that several men *the ones I don't know*
have been duplicating *your active workings… so*
my Poems and *I could own them. It would be like you and I*
are going door to door *or maybe like I am unearthing your bones*
selling Pirate copies *as if they were mine, every one*
of them.

On the 9th March, 1922, *decades ago*
a Warrant was issued *between our lifetimes*
for the arrest of a man who *sounds crazy I know but*
had travelled *in a shaft of light*
through Yorkshire, *quite a bit farther than*
Notts and Derbyshire and *anywhere, you*
sold thousands of copies *and I fused at the core*
of my Poem.

He also stated in some cases *beyond genetics*
that he was authorized *mystically or cosmically*
by me to sell them. *you might say*
This is entirely a falsehood, *it's undeniable*
as I employ NO agents. *I am, like you, drilling*
All my Poems are *in a similar vein, sometimes*
Copyright and fully protected *to a fault*
and are entirely my own *but these days that*
composition and property *isn't enough, it must be a Poem*

and every one has
my own Photograph
(as above)
on the front
of it.

Should an imposter call
and offer any of my Poems
for sale,
will you kindly inform
the Police
and oblige.

to be mined as if it were
revealing your bones
there's that thread again
on the face
a fissure in everything I write

I will read your words
not to assess their value
but to fathom my own, and
the Muse
or anyone else who might answer

ARMEN DAVOUDIAN

Guidance Patrol

for my mother, Arax

When the black van pulled over, my hand was in yours.
They thought I was your lover: my hand was in yours.

When she yanked up your headscarf, when you fell to the ground,
when the lights loomed above her, my hand was in yours.

When they marched us here, when we crossed or drowned in
your namesake river, my hand was in yours.

"A grown man"—"My son"—"Bi namoos, haram!"
Lest the faithful discover my hand was in yours.

When Old Julfa was burning and drunk on fear
—we're still hungover—my hand was in yours.

You were the wife of Lot. I was the salt of your body.
Though I'm not a believer, my hand was in yours.

"Who speaks of the Armenians?" Let our gravestones crumble
so they can uncover my hand was in yours.

Note:

In 1606, the Armenians of Old Julfa were forced to cross the Arax river
and resettle in Iran.

ERIN LAMBERT HARTMAN

Bruised Fruit

I travel as I live: among the hurt
and hurried, though not as breathless

as the British woman who darts past me
in Dulles, who later can't stand

or fully bend to catch her bracelets when
they break away from her wrist

in the restroom where she says to
leave the charms behind some stalls.

It's your psoas, I lean over the sink
to explain and, to be friendly, try winking

when I say, *I'd bet on it,* though I feel
I'm really wincing now that I'm estranged

from family and have only my husband
to notice when I'm gone too long.

He finds me down some dimly-lit hallway,
helping her to stretch and stand again.

What else have we to find? Bruised fruit.
Aspirin to ease the lag between time.

What else can we take that won't be taken?
Become a burden once there?

Standing at the gate and wanting to leave
all we carry untouched, we look

to ourselves in the windows
and into the black night beyond

where I retrieve this memory
of a minister who lived in the fourth

stage of cancer for more than twenty years.
We met two months before her death;

her right arm swollen with lymph, its
weight and texture as unyielding

as the hardy pith in winter squash.
I would not let her leave

until her sleeve hung loose
and the cuff stopped chaffing.

You're worth your weight in gold,
she told me but I pretended

she was you, every one of you saying,
though we knew, as did she,

her arm would swell again
before she made it home.

JENNIE ZIVERK CARR

Cradled

There is nothing more quiet than white,
and then pink,
and then red.

To lose what was never yours
While mourning dreams.

Cradled in silence
It was empty –
my womb.

YOUNG WRITER AWARD WINNER

COURTNEY CONRAD

Jamaica Grapples with 'Till Death Do Us Part'

after Nadine Wilson-Harris

Mama seh when him start wid him foolishness / yuh fi boil di honey and pour it inna him work shoes / crush laxatives like ginga and sprinkle it ova him ital stew / mash up di scotch bonnet pepper and mix it wid lime juice and dash it inna him eye / barefoot / chicken chest / holey boxered yute uses yardstick to beat breadfruit / unknowing of delicate pickings / handles women and mangoes the same / sucks until hair thins and complexions fade / yute's hand miggle lick likkle gyal inna back during freeze tag / aims for her head during dandy shandy / father says *stop bawl / yuh know seh him neva mean it* / triangular rage leaving behind grieving mother / *I tell him don't bother go do nuttin foolish* / they go to church every sunday / married for a decade / but in the dead of the night / *woi jesus* / dormant tongue cannot babble / but bredren says *a nuff man she keke wid* / gossip circle forms / bodies wiggling in seats the way one does when worms fill stomachs / group wash out releasing acidic accusations / *him go out go get pickney and di woman still neva lef him* / badges and their black spit shine shoes too good for country dust / potholes and overflowing gully water / residents say *police fi do better dem always wait till something happen before dem tek action* / what else can a mother say when she fears her daughter will be made pocketable for the sky

JO DAVIS

Fit for Work

In the lesson that was meant to be about poetry I said look
This is Stephen Hawking. He had a lot to say about the universe
And his mouth stopped working. He had a lot to write
About the universe and his hands stopped moving.
He had a lot of work to do and his body stopped working.
All he could move were his eyes and they saw the universe.
So we made him a voice to tell the universe with. And we
Listened where his eyes looked and we knew what they saw.

We could have just
Shrugged and laid him to look at the ceiling. But
We worked and he looked and he showed us the sky.
You still gawped at the man sat askew in his chair.
You heard what he did, knew the broader sky he showed us:
'That's sad,' you said.

SUSANNAH HART

In Memoriam

Never much given to sentimentality, my mother,
when I ask her, says she doesn't see the point
of monuments. They were both cremated, she says,
and it didn't seem worth putting up a plaque
or stone of any kind. After all, who would be going
to Bedfordshire again? And my grandmother
on my father's side, well, she thinks she was cremated
too. If there's a memorial to her anywhere, perhaps
my aunt would know. Or would have known, at least,
when she could remember things like that. As for
my father's father, she has no idea what they did
with him or where. She can't recall a funeral.

I'm certain there's no record of where my father,
or what was left of him, resides. She didn't want
the body repatriated, thought it unlikely to be him.
So he remained, along with all the other unclaimed bits
and pieces, somewhere in a Lagos suburb. No,
she was never sentimental. We never visited
a special bench or laid flowers by an engraved brass.
But every year, on that day in late November,
she'd turn to the In Memoriam in *The Times*
where, without fail, the pilot's widow placed
a notice. She'd read it to herself, and then to us,
as if that remembering took the load from her.

LOIS P. JONES

When Two Men, All Pupil No Sclera

For months after the shooting death of Ahmaud Arbery, a 25-year-old Black man pursued by armed white residents of a … South Georgia neighborhood… no arrests were made. ~NYT

He was simply interested in the bones of the house. ~ Aunt of Ahmaud Arbery.

I've seen these crows before.   Perched on the laundry line. Sheltered in the shade of a ghost sheet. Black as black's pupil and never a membrane of summer's reason.   I've seen crow, crow down and crawl crafty. I've seen them fly like night in broad daylight hunting for an eye. And what the running man sees in his last moments is a wing so wide he can't escape and somewhere close its pupil – not chatoyant but flat black as empty. He sees the shadow of talons before the piercing. What he saw before – windows waiting for glass. He knew the fresh scent of pine inside the bones of a house being built. Any man will stand beneath the new timbers of a home and press their palms to its dirt. Any man will run to feel the wind move through them. A predator knows this. That's how the crow opens up a man when he dies, eating the soft tissue of what he sees, then burying the rest.

76

I

If this is what we know, then the year is 1976 and the air is thick
with everything coming. If this is not a war, then there will be
no need for an enemy. If there is a hero, then there will be death.
If history, being what it is, demands a hero. We could use the
DeLorean to jump back into time. If it were only that simple.
Then this text would be the experiment in which we are studying
time. It passes slower the more you are moving. I used to be
a scientist. Consider, for example, light emitted from a moving
source has a lower frequency. I am moving. When you change
your speed, you rotate the direction of time. This is how time

II

behaves when it is rotated - it becomes relative. We will begin
with a plane because you might have heard one pass by your
window. What is flying but a way to climb the air? We are at
30,000 feet on flight 139. What do you know of the Revolutionary
Cell? What do you know of Athens airport? What do you know
about Operation Thunderbolt? You may or may not have heard
of Yoni and what happened in 1976. In the movie, Yoni is the hero.
The known enemies are the terrorists lead by Bose. We are seven
days away from the 4th of July but this is not an American story.
We are heading to a foreign town on an airport runway on the

III

same day The Real Thing tops the charts with *You To Me Are Everything*.
The song will spend three weeks at number one. You might be asking
What does that band have to do with the terrorist operation?
It is in the first line. *I would take the stars out of the sky for you*
I want to tell you about the sky. I want to tell you about the
sounds of leaving. I may talk about Basquiat and what he knew
of Icarus. I don't know where to begin so I may jump around in
search of a source code, in search of a known life, in search of
fire and something to displace us. There will be foreign dying.
But before we begin with these elements here is an advert.

DAVID SWANN

A Hill in November

Strange to recall the whales here at dusk
on an allotment far from the ocean

but when my call draws no answer
out of our neighbour, I sense from his face,

lost in contemplation of a brazier,
that he's found something in the flames

more real than I am, only an acquaintance
stumbling through the failing light

to fix a net over the chard and sweep leaves
into the compost bin. Most of the news

from the world is bleak, so I've come here
for the crumbling comforts of November:

the tall cosmos shedding their last petals
in the breeze, the final apples of fall.

That neighbour of mine, lost to the mysteries
of his blaze, once let slip while stoned

that he lost a child long ago, and never
mentioned it again. That's the way we prefer it

up here on the hill – to discuss sprouts
when we describe our grief, to make cabbage-flies

the emblem of our damage. Those whales, though –
why do they rise through me now? We'd lifted

our thumbs on a cliff-side road and gained
access into a wonder. The couple were grey

and bright-eyed, and excited to narrate
their day. They'd seen whales out on the bay,

a great many of them, raising their flukes
and bashing the waves, in breach upon breach –

'Treasure,' she called them, the wife,
a German with silver plaits. 'Which no person

can ever own,' said her man, keeping
his thousand-yard gaze on the waves, still hoping

they'd gleam again in his day, though the less
they gleamed, the more their value increased.

I'd known then as I knew from our neighbour's
face. There beyond the reef and up here

on the hill: they were measuring their losses
in the deeps. Quiet now, I slip away,

leaving the man by his fire, its flame trembling
as I fumble with the gate, careful not to spill

the last six raspberries, a little damp
on my palm: treasures, found in darkness.

JANE THOMAS

We Real Spinsters

After Gwendolyn Brooks

We extra rib. We
Sans crib. We

Gold Miss. We
Single bliss. We

No trouble. We
No strife. We

Have bankroll. We
Birth control. We

Not 'erindoors. We
Marianne Moores. We

No WAG. We
No hag. We

Speak out. We
Sometimes shout. We

Riot Grrrls. We
Are pearls. We

Are waves. We
No slaves. We

Spare Rib. We
Women's Lib. We

Two halves. We
Different paths. We

Jane Austen. We
Marry Boston. We

Emily Dickinson. We
Full citizen. We

Thread spinners. We
Are breadwinners. We

No Earls. We
Golden Girls.

JESSICA TRAYNOR

Becoming Catwoman

My mother was a secretary too, like Selina Kyle,
before Christopher Walken pushed her out a window –
(Selina, not my mother). My seven-year-old self
watched her body slam through awning after awning
(not my mother's body, but Selina's),
splatting onto Tim Burton's snowy alleyway.
Then the cats come, envelop her like the fur coat
that hung in the wardrobe at home, the one
she always said was suspiciously tabby-striped
(my mother, not Selina) and they lick and lick her
and somehow this reknits her shattered spine,
her arms and legs swivel into place but her glasses,
her large owl-eye glasses (my mother's, Selina's)
are smashed and this is the worst, just the *worst* day –
being pushed out the window! By a man with
a strange speech tic no one mentions
because bosses can talk like bosses and push women
out of sky scrapers and it's, like,
bad day at the office, amirite? And up she gets
and makes her way home to her little girl apartment
so we can see she's just been playing at being a woman –
she's built herself a toyshop to get lost in,
(Selina, not my mother) and she freaks
the absolute fuck out splattering walls
with black paint and smashing toys and as a little girl
(me, not my mother, not Selina) this is just devastating,
because it feels like we aren't allowed
to have anything soft –
no knitted kittens or kit-cat klocks –
because it makes us weak and the only way to stop
men with Struwwelpeter hair
from pushing us out of skyscrapers
(me, my mother, Selina) is by killing
everything dear to us so that no one else can.

eating god for breakfast

we are at the kitchen table eating eggs, and god
i love sundays. i imagine keeping sunday so close to me
tattooed on my sternum, or across my knuckles, sun
day, in two easy halves. my girlfriend says,
i have got diarrhea because i am on my period
and leaves me thinking about production and waste
about how we are all every day coming out of and going back into the ground
everybody emerging from and returning to the earth over breakfast,
which makes death feel normal, like breathing.
and yes, i would like a baby —
do i mind if it comes out of my body?
is it an insult to say no after spending my whole life
shitting and pissing and bleeding and coughing and vomiting
god says, why not this? then every meal, every moment, you are turning
your toast and eggs into something alive
(but i am doing that here, now), like a coral reef
growing in the deep sea sunlight,
or, of course, like a bud, opening.
everything has been very domestic this year,
so it's nice to think about, at the table. and i do
just love to have breakfast with you. etta james sings
I want a sunday kind of love, and that's nice, it's all so nice.

CHARLIN McISAAC

Manischewitz Night

We have to drink the entire bottle of Manischewitz in the alley or we will be out Seven Canadian Dollars which is actually only One Canadian Dollar and Sixteen Canadian Cents because there are six of us. Jennifer is a Capricorn so she is in charge of this even though no one has discussed it, and she has to pull Kiva back into the alleyway because if she starts hollering at men in cars she's gonna draw too much attention to us and this entire operation is gonna blow wide open. Abby is wasted and freezing and desperate to get inside and she is hopping one foot to another in her little brown boots to keep warm. Cameron says did it stain my lips and Jennifer says yes and Thalia says no girl and that's sort of a shit-hits-the-fan moment, but we absolutely *have* to shut the fuck up guys or else someone is going to find out that there are six college-aged women destroying some kosher wine right outside Boots & Bourbon and we will *not* get to square dance with Sadie, who is trying to have some sort of Calgary-ass birthday in Toronto in the middle of winter.

Jennifer is fixing her earring and spitting *okay girls we are LATE* and you can see every word misty in the air and you can also see Jennifer's type-A brain fully having a whole entire meltdown at the thought of being fashionably behind schedule, which is actually so delightful of her and this is honestly why I keep you around like I'm *obsessed* with you, Jen. Kiva cannot feel fear nor cold and is going to take off her shirt, she's saying it, she's like pointing to a guy parked in front of Boots like: guys I'm going to show that Uber driver my nipple ring, no men have seen it yet, and we have to be like... you will actually get hypothermia from that babe you can't, you *cannot* do that. When she shows it, flipping her shirt up with pure mischief, his eyes melt instantly, boiling and bubbling in his sockets and dribbling like molten egg whites down his cheeks, which is so awful to see and it's like, if you're going to get a cursed nipple ring you should at least take it out when you're drunk because things like this *are* going to happen, they tell you that at the literal appointment.

Kiva's like I am going to get this thing SOOOOOO INFECTED and we are like GIRL THE CURSE IS GOING TO GET *BAD* IF YOU

28

INFECT THE PIERCING and Kiva is like I didn't go to theatre school to *not get an infected nipple piercing!!!!!* which, what does that even mean first of all, and second of all Kiva, you're actually gorgeous and to be honest the middle part is working, like I know you were kinda on the fence but you actually look like Mila Kunis right now.

The Uber driver drives away, which is super hard for him now that his eyeballs are in a puddle in his lap, and Cameron says that's sad and Thalia is like he'll be *fiiiine*, which... he will, but like, that sucks for right now. Ohhhhh my god I could go get onion rings after this, also, if you guys are down. Okay. Who's got the bottle.

Thalia has the bottle and it's pretty much done and Sadie's best friend Morgan has sent us all a text like THE OBELISK IS ACTIVATED . HER EYES ARE GLOWING . ADVANCE TO THE HIVE . which is sooooo fucking Morgan but whatever, she's just being catty and like won't stop talking about her semester abroad. Thalia downs the rest of the wine and we are officially good to go, except fuck our ACTUAL lives Abby's left her corporeal form again. This bitch can not keep it together.

It's been a solid five months of this ritual and we are *tired* and DESPERATE for the equinox because it is downright exhausting taking care of your friend when she splits her consciousness into fucking Knife Dimension or whatever. She's talking to Invisible Dave who lives in the air again and she's counting spells in threes under her breath and we're like tapping her on her shoulder like ok kiddo time to pay cover but poor Abby is pretending to stab Invisible Dave and tar is spilling out of her ears and mouth and she *just* got this coat. Cameron gets the duct tape from her purse and we tape the oven mitts onto Abby's hands so she can't do any structural damage when her claws manifest and she opens her mouth to scream a scream that only Thalia and I can hear and then we start writing down her hex repetitions in the Notes app of Cameron's phone just in case there are any patterns or clues that her doctor needs to know about.

When it's over we clean up the tar a bit and stow the oven mitts back in Cameron's bag and it's very much like a 'noooo you look fine' moment because if Abby could see herself right now she would not be interested in entering the bar and we are *not* going home before midnight. Morgan is in our texts again with like, *just exclamation marks* and a picture of a tequila shot and an angry face emoji and it's like we are *literally going as fast as we can* with a cursed nipple ring and a split consciousness in tow, not like we didn't bend over backward for you when your knee turned into sentient zirconium six months ago but whatever.

The bouncer is *not* impressed and it's like, I get it, we are covered in black slime and our lips are stained purple but lowkey this is a look that a lot of girls are going for right now and ours just happened to be caused by evil magics and that is not our fault. He raises his eyebrows at Abby's ID which is fair because she looks approx thirteen and some of her claws are still retracting and changing back into fingers and she is TURNT but he lets us in when she throws him an extra ten dollar bill from her January Budget Envelope and we. are. INNNN

Sadie's birthday obelisk is like GLOWING she looks AMAZING. She is wearing a bedazzled cowboy hat of her own creation and she is grinding up on her obelisk like the literal sweet-angel-baby-*national treasure* of Canada. The pale jade glow is refracting off shot glasses and her hat and her earrings—hoops, *iconic*—and she is belting the current playlist with her signature closed-eyes-aspirate-Hs. A queen. A literal birthday queen. Morgan is furious and angrily buys us all shots for being late. We can't explain Abby because we don't wanna bring the mood down so we just tip our lil treats back and try not to gag on cheap alcohol and we all take turns saying nice things about Sadie which can I just sayyyyyyy, did you *know* your birthday eyes would glow green this year because it's like...the dress. The dress of it all. Fantastic, chic, alien forest cowboy goddess WHOM!!!!! You are a gift to humanity, you are the birthday babe of 4ever.

Kiva immediately finds someone with drugs and then does the deepest plié known to mankind and just starts shaking it on the dance floor. I catch her eye like yesss girl and she opens her mouth and winks and points to the nipple ring under her shirt like *I am definitely going to show this to someone in the bathroom later* and it's like, live your WHOLE truth babe!!!! Inspired. We are all Making It Work on the dance floor, we are Giving It!! Sadie's song comes on and the light from her birthday obelisk ripples through the crowd and we all start square dancing like marionettes but SEXY!! I can feel my arms moving like tentacles and my little legs are doing a heel-toe-cross thing like the ultimate cowboy BABE, like put some damn GINGHAM on me right now!

Abby is doing her little dance where like, she's trapped in a net but she's figuring it out, and it looks sooooo cute and good and sweet. Her little brown boots actually have no tar on them at all—how is it possible?!—and she is grinning a little weasel grin and the two of us say our little chant which goes *There's something about it, There's something about it, There's something about it!* with some arms in the air like we're brushing away cobwebs and Sadie's obelisk must be giving off some amazingly powerful birthday magics because there is a moment where like I swear to god there's like a nice cool breeze through the crowd with like sparkles, even? And it smells like purple plaid shirts and when you both like the same hummus.

Suddenly Abby's eyes look at the corner of the room and her face goes rigid and I touch her hand super lightly like heyyy it's okay we're having fun! And she says nothing and I glance back at the corner to be like lol there's nothing there don't worry! And when I turn back her mouth is moving a tiny little bit and I *just know* she is murmuring those hex repetitions again and maybe we shouldn't have brought her here but she really wanted to come and she deserves a normal night and it's not her fault she got trapped in a ritual.

Abby slides a knife out from her top and it's almost like she *shrugs* right before she stabs me in the leg and if you have never been stabbed in the leg before on a dance floor in the middle of a country bar can I just say you have no idea what you're talking about and you should probably just shut up on the whole issue because it actually hurts a *lot*. And my friends are watching me like keel over and being like okay okay don't be too dramatic and don't make it weird for her and Abby is counting her spells on her fingers and the knife is like fully in my leg like just *hanging there* first of all and Morgan is giving this look like don't you fucking ruin Sadie's birthday and Kiva is giving this look like if you make this a big deal you are going to *fuck over the friend group*.

I try to smile but the knife is in my leg and it probably just looks like when you're breaking in new heels and you have to be like 'yeah I totally love these' because you *will* love them eventually even though they are murdering your feet, like, *now*. And Morgan says something like 'ohmygod Abby you're soooo spacey' and Kiva is like 'this is actually claaaaassic' — which let's be clear: It Isn't! — and Kiva leans her head on top of Abby's head and I'm looking at Abby's hands like *is she going to grow her claws, do we need the mitts, do we need the tape*, and Abby is just staring straight ahead, right through me, letting out a stream of silent hexes at hyperspeed. Sadie has her hands in the air and is singing a song that's like *Country song/ specific image from my small town/ old truck very sexy/ girls drinkin' beer in shorts* and so maybe this is over, maybe it's fine and we'll just move past it, and like on the one hand I'm wasted so like it's not that bad in terms of pain but it's also like, not *not* a knife and legs have... arteries, probably. Like, Statistically.

I make some signature AM I BEING CRAZY? eye contact with Cameron and notice she literally has her hand in her bag like DEFINITELY going for the mitts but not knowing whether to do it or not, and I'm like widening my eyes like YES the mitts that's literally what I was thinking but Kiva has taken Abby's hands and is trying to teach her how to remember her caught-in-a-net dance and it's like maybe working? And there aren't any claws? So I'm probably overreacting and we should just hydrate or something. And as we leave to go to the bar Morgan is like 'JUST BY THE WAY, SADIE DRINKS *VODKA* OR *CIDER*' which is like, you're being aggressive Morgan, but we go get some water and stumble to the bathroom.

In the bathroom, a super drunk stranger with curly hair and a snake tattoo holds my face and says 'This KNIFE!!!!!!!! You are HOT!!!!! I could never pull that off' and I am suddenly crying for real and she's like 'you HAVE to DUMP HIM' and I'm shaking my head like noooo this isn't about a guy and Cameron is ushering me into a stall and drunkenly mistyping shit into her Google search on her phone like KNFE STAB TWKE OUT????? and BEST FREIDN MURDR DANCFLKOOR????? and I'm looking at the knife and it's so fucking ugly and stupid and it completely fucks up my outfit and it's *not* hot and it just like, sucks to be told that it's hot when you're in a bathroom drunk crying which is literally the least hot thing you can possibly do in the first place and it's just *fucking annoying* having to deal with this when it was supposed to just be a fun Manischewitz Night in conjunction with also our friend's birthday at a country bar.

Cameron is stroking my hair and scrolling through articles and I suggest just taking the knife out and like maybe we can put it in a bag or something and then later when we're all sober we can talk to Abby about it and Cam does that thing where she like instantly snaps out of her drunkenness and then says super ominously 'yeah but also we specifically hid all painkillers and sharp objects so how does she even have that?' My mascara is everywhere and Cameron sprays me with her perfume, very no-nonsense governess, very *Sensuous by Estée Lauder by Mary Poppins*, while still looking at her phone and saying hmmmm for a long time.

I take a shuddering breath and whimper 'Does it say I can take it outttt' and Cam says 'It *says* we should go to the hospital,' and Snake Tattoo Girl is listening from outside the stall and is like 'For the record I literally thought you did it on purpose, it makes you look heroic!!' and then she says 'Also my ex was in med school and you shouldn't take knives out on your own.'

I am not going to let Abby fuck up the night. I am not going to fuck up *Abby's* night by making this a big deal. If we take the knife out we can just put some toilet paper on it or something and keep dancing. People clean cuts with alcohol all the time and there's *literally* more alcohol here than there is at the hospital, so probably we should just stay. Cameron is on WebMD shaking her head like noooo this is definitely a hospital visit based on size of knife and location of injury and then she says 'Hey did she say anything before she split into Knife Dimension or did you see any warning signs or movements?' and I'm like I LITERALLY AM DRUNK AND I DON'T WANNA HAVE TO BE A SCIENTIST LITERALLY TWENTY FOUR SEVEN SO I DON'T KNOW and Cam says 'I know' and it's actually kind of soothing because we're just stuck in hell together.

I try to take the knife out but Cameron sees me out of the corner of her eye and says NOPE and Snake Tattoo Girl says 'Did she try to take the knife out!!' and Cameron says WE DON'T KNOW YOU and I say I JUST WANNA DANCE, STOP TELLING ME WHAT TO DO and Snake Tattoo Girl says 'Okay girly I'm gonna leave you alone but don't forget: you. are. beautiful!!!!!' and Cameron is like 'I'm gonna call an ambulance' and I'm like thinking about how sad Sadie's gonna be because it's her birthday and how pissed Morgan's gonna be *also because* it's Sadie's birthday and how Abby might literally be out there totally normal now and we could all just get onion rings later and it wouldn't even have to be a thing if I just take the knife out and remind myself that hey, sometimes our friends get trapped in rituals and it's normal and it's really actually kind of selfish of me to even CONSIDER ruining an *entire friend group* just because of one LITTLE public stabbing.

'Only a doctor can take out the knife,' says Cameron. Her phone is away now.

'Well, I'm not leaving,' I say. I feel a little bit lighter and also a little bit more present. Not sure if Blood Loss or Sobriety Kicking In.

Cameron's eyes are huge and she's doing the thing with her mouth where she obviously wants to bite her lip in judgment but the celebrities say not to do that because it encourages chapping and dryness, so she just sort of presses her lips together and raises her perfectly manicured brows.

On the way out of the bathroom stall we see that Snake Tattoo Girl is in front of the mirror pretending to put on lipstick but the lipstick isn't even open she's just like, miming it and watching the mirror for us and when she recognizes us she's like, 'So are you gonna go to the hospital or are you staying?' and Cameron rolls her eyes but doesn't say anything and I start washing my hands because they have a bit of my blood on them and I just say like, 'I'm gonna keep it in' super casual, and Snake Tattoo Girl says 'Yessss, no party foul!' with a huge smile and uncaps her lipstick to reveal that it's just a tiny carrying case for a neatly rolled joint and she presents it to me like a bouquet of roses and says 'for ur pain' in a small voice. I laugh a bit and dry off my hands to accept the lil joint and I say thank you and she says 'That knife is gonna hurt *so much* when it comes out later. Like don't look at it when they take it out, you don't even wanna see it' and I say thank you again and she says, 'You honestly could just keep it in forever, like I *wish*, right?' and I say uh huh and laugh and then we go back out into the main room.

Sadie is on the bull and her glowing birthday obelisk is quaking a little. Morgan is cheering her on and GLARING at anyone who cheers louder. Thalia and Jennifer are chatting with too much eye contact. They will probably make out later. Kiva is nowhere to be found, but there is a man desperately pawing at the ground, trying to scoop up his eye sludge beside the bar. After a little bit, the knife actually doesn't feel like much anymore. Like. Honestly you can barely notice it when you're dancing. Cameron is stuck to my elbow, cautious and fierce, and she doesn't say anything when Abby asks where I got the cute knife. The song switches and all of a sudden we are trying to shake off the invisible net. *There's something about it! There's something about it! There's something about it!*

ADAM WELCH

A breath is a motion is the air rising is water flowing

It was up to the two of them to save the planet. Aster believed this deeply and so Vince had to believe it too. The planet-saving was everyone's responsibility, of course, but also, somehow, theirs in particular. In Aster's mind, all these little things they were doing – the conscientious recycling, the relentless re-using, the sudden switching to low-energy, phthalate-free everything – was building a better future, for each other, and for humanity. He believed this despite the evidence. Despite everything that had happened, and was happening. This is why they had to sleep in a second-hand bed.

A man called round with it, on a Saturday afternoon. It was grey, and wet outside. It always was. They lived by a river in a rainy part of the country, where people drank lots of tea and said 'that'll do' and 'never mind'. They had moved there the week before, because Aster needed more space, and more nature, and because Vince had fucked a guy at work, and this had been the obvious solution. The man with the bed was called Pete. He came in a white van.

'Who is that?' said Vince, rinsing dishes in a bucket, watching, out the kitchen window, as he saw the white dot appear on the horizon.

'Pete,' said Aster, pulling on wellies, in the dank hallway.

'What's he doing here?' said Vince, in a slightly louder voice.

'What do you think?' called Aster.

The house was a few miles out from the nearest village. It had been a ruin, was now a work-in-progress. Aster had found it by chance, through satellite photographs, because this is what he had spent a lot of time doing, before, on his bad days: sitting on the laptop, on Zoom Earth and Google Maps. He would sit for hours, his cheeks sucked in, his overgrown hair tucked behind his ears, his grey-speckled eyebrows furrowed, toggling the magnification. He would fret about the sun-baked plains and shrinking rainforests. He would sigh at the extent of the urban sprawl, spot alarming patterns in the skies. The house had been the tiniest cluster of pixels on the screen, then, as Aster zoomed in, a grey blur between two fields, then, as he zoomed some more, a small cluster of abandoned buildings, next to black slick of water. This, Aster had announced, was an incredible opportunity.

The van juddered along the long, muddy track that led from the main road to their front garden. As it got closer, Vince watched it bouncing up and down on the uneven ground, swerving from left to right to avoid deep puddles. It pulled into the front garden, swung carefully round the tarpaulin-covered piles and then went into reverse, backing up its rear doors to the front of the house. A face, bearded, smiling, leaned out the driver's window, and nodded at as Aster emerged from the front door, in his mismatched tracksuit.

'Hi, Pete is it?' said Aster, waving.

'It's Pete,' said Pete.

'Pete, right?' said Aster.

In the front garden, under the tarpaulins, they had more junk than they would ever need. An old window that, Aster said, could be turned into a cold frame. Three bicycle wheels that would make a decent trellis. Empty paint cans, spindly twigs and lengths of plastic tubing that, Aster assured Vince, were going to become a bee hotel. Old pallets to make raised beds. Concrete rubble for crazy paving. The trouble with crazy paving, Aster said, was getting it just crazy enough, but not too crazy. In the kitchen, Vince squeezed the scourer, and continued to watch.

'So,' said Pete, climbing down from the driver's seat. 'Where do you want this bed?'

*   *   *

It would be explained, later, that about 1,000 miles to the north-east, somewhere below Iceland, the sea had been warm. The sun had been heating it up, all summer, and though the days were now getting shorter, the water was cooling far slower than the landmasses that surrounded it. As the sea held on to its warmth, it also radiated it outwards, giving generously to the air above it, which, receiving the warmth, rose upwards. As the warm air rose, it left space that had to be filled, which is why colder air rushed in from colder places, from snow-covered mountain sides and creaking glaciers and lonely grey coastlines where the wind whipped dizzied birds towards the clifftops. The cold air rushed to fill the space and the warm air vaulted out of it, and at the point where warm and cold met, and spun around each other, there was suddenly not much of either, far above, in the atmosphere, pushing down. This is what, it would be explained, later, is known as an area of low pressure. It's a description

36

that sounds a lot more relaxing than the reality it represents: an unsettled sky, occasional headaches, rain, hail, snow.

* * *

Before the house, and the bed, they had lived in a flat, in a city, in a drier part of the country where people said 'Excuse me!' and 'Absolutely!'. In the city, everything had been shiny and brand new, and once you were done with it, you threw it away, and forgot about it. Vince had worked in forecasting, which had been big business, in that part of the country, because everyone had everything they wanted, and the real money was in working out what people would want next. Aster had worked too, as a primary school teacher, but he'd been signed off after a particularly bad day on which he taught the kids more than they should really have had to deal with. Since then, he hadn't been working at all, just wandering from room to room, with his laptop, mumbling about the polar ice caps. It had been a wasteful life, incredibly so. But so much of life is waste, as Vince had argued, when they had their big talk.

'If you're looking for an explanation, I don't have an explanation, exactly' said Vince, from one side of the kitchen table.

They mostly used the kitchen for fighting, not cooking. They had bought the flat off-plan. They were the first people that had ever lived there. The oven was clean and the pans were still in their packaging. Vince was too busy to read all the recipes and source all the ingredients. Aster was too depressed. They ate takeaways. They stacked up the empty boxes, next to the fridge.

'So it was just… random?' said Aster, dead-eyed, from the other side of the table, which had been shipped from another, colder northern European country, despite the many other tables available nearby.

'I was very drunk,' said Vince, 'and I lost control, momentarily.'

Aster rolled his eyes, and opened up his laptop. It was a laptop designed to last for six years, then self-destruct catastrophically.

'I suppose, I was thinking, at the time,' said Vince, 'that there was no real reason that I should deny myself the experience. That anyone should.'

Aster shook his head, sadly, as he typed in his login. The truth was, Vince hadn't been thinking. It had felt like thinking had been holding him back for too long. The truth was the opportunity had presented itself, and it had seemed absurd, but it had also felt like not taking it would be like surrendering, like accepting that nothing new or unexpected would ever happen again.

'Ok, right.' said Aster, stroking the touchpad. 'So the past ten years… not a reason?'

Ten years was longer than anything lasted, in the city.

'No,' said Vince. 'I mean, yes, you're right, you're right. It totally is. But, what I mean is, what I meant to say is…'

'What?'

The ridiculous thing was the guy in question, the guy who Vince fucked, was not someone he had ever really liked. They had worked together, briefly, on the future of feminine hygiene. The guy's hair was slicked with gel and his teeth were far too white, and his skin was smooth and waxy, like he'd just been unwrapped from plastic. The two of them had clashed in meetings, exchanged passive-aggressive emails, spent many hours complaining about each other's communication style, and then, when it was all over, when they'd done their pitch, gone to the pub with everyone else. It had been little more than a fumble in a toilet cubicle, seven pints later: inelegant, badly lit, poorly executed, very uncomfortable. The guy's pubic hair was trimmed to sharp, dark bristles. His crotch smelled of deodorant.

'I just sometimes have this idea, or this sense, you know, that I'm not making the most of my life,' said Vince, getting up from the table, walking to the window.

'You're unbelievable.'

'What I'm saying,' said Vince, 'is we only have a certain amount of time, and we only get to have it once, and isn't it kind of weird that, in this limited time, rather than… open ourselves… you know, to experience, we just do the same things, again and again and again?'

'So, what are you saying. You're bored?'

'No, that's not it.'

'I don't believe you.'

'It's not.'

'So prove it.'

That's when Aster turned his laptop round, to show him the house.

*   *   *

Two thousand miles south of the area of low pressure, it would later be explained, was something quite the opposite: a wide stretch of space where the atmosphere was thick, and dense. It could be seen on the satellite images, a giant, a dark oval of near-black-blue with wispy clouds circling around its edges. The oval started off, at the beginning of the summer, hovering over the Azores. But as the months rolled on it shifted, spinning itself calmly westwards, until it reached Bermuda. The oval, it would be explained, is what you call an area of high pressure, because it contained many towering cubic metres of cooling air that had been warmed in the tropics and was now collecting there, tumbling earthwards. The resulting sensation, at the centre of this area, was actually pleasant and holiday-like. Here, people enjoyed clear skies, warm breezes, a persistent, enveloping sensation of calm.

*   *   *

In the rainy part of the country, the rain was as acid as vinegar. In the village, you could see its effects: the melted pockmarks on the bricks of the yellow stone buildings; the withered ivy that clung to their sides. They both saw this immediately because the day after the move, they drove into the village, and walked around, searching. They had left everything behind, except the takeaway boxes, because, Aster said, they might come in handy, and it was important to reuse plastic. Now they needed various things – materials; homeware; furniture – but Aster only wanted any of it if it could be responsibly sourced. They peered into front gardens and skips, looking for cast-off sideboards and occasional stools. They scoured the shelves of the charity shops, hoping for tableware, a kettle, anything.

They had some luck, but not a lot. In this part of the country, unlike the other, people did not just get rid of things for the sake of it. All they threw away, here, was genuine junk. So that's what Vince and Aster had to make do with, loading up the car with the window frame, the paint cans, the bicycle wheels. After two hours Aster was still smiling, but his expression was fixed and strained. Vince was exhausted, by the walking, by the situation, and as it began to rain again, said:

'Maybe we should just go home.'

They didn't go home, though, because Aster wouldn't be defeated. They went to the Co-Operative and stared at the bulletin board, because, Aster said, there was sure to be someone offloading insulation, or old wood floors, or roof tiles. The bulletin board was by the entrance, just behind the tills. To get to it they had to walk past a fridge full of snacks. As they skimmed over the notices, Vince's stomach rumbled, and he thought, longingly, of sandwiches in windowed boxes and bite-sized chorizo in waxed paper bags, and other things that, Aster had made clear, were no longer part of their world, disposable packaging being one of his chief torments.

'It doesn't just disappear,' he had said, on many of the worst days. 'It's all got to go somewhere. Don't you ever think of that?'

In the Co-Operative, Aster stared intently at the bulletin board, pulling tabs off paper notices, his lips pressed together, grimly. Vince shifted slowly from foot to foot, looking around, clocking every security camera.

The river ran through the village. There was a stone bridge across it. In strong sunlight it looked picturesque and magical, but in the rain you couldn't ignore the wide grey streaks down the side, the smell of sewage drifting upwards. Once Aster had got enough numbers, they stood on the bridge together, back-to-back, looking out, in opposite directions. As he listened to Aster punching a number into his phone, Vince reached into his anorak pocket, and pulled out the small packet he had stuffed in there, quickly, on the way out of the Co-Operative. As he had done so, simply giving into the impulse, he'd felt it. That same sense of 'why couldn't it be?'; 'why shouldn't it?'; 'why not?'. He had not been able to think of a reason. His heart was still thumping. On the bridge, he opened the shiny packet with great delicacy. The silver foil barely crinkled as he dipped his fingers inside, taking great care not to make any noise. He snuck a glance back at Aster, who was leaning over the other side of the bridge, his elbows resting on the wall. Aster was staring upwards at the darkening sky, and yelling into his phone, which he clasped to one ear:

'Hi, is that Pete? I'm calling about the notice —'

Aster talked on, but Vince turned back and tuned him out, selecting a yellow corn puff from the packet and slowly placing it in the centre of his mouth, on the widest part of his tongue, sucking, not crunching. The taste was startling, sour and salty. It was a genius thing, more real than reality. The tang of it rocketed straight to the centre of his brain. He sucked it slowly, savouring the crackling, fizzing sensation as his saliva soaked into the puff's starchy walls, wearing them down, melting them to nothing. Then he had another one. And then he had another. And another. When he was finished, barely thinking about it, he dropped the bag over the bridge, into the river. He watched, letting his face fall slack, as the packet floated away, twisting and glinting in the sluggish current.

* * *

Higher up, far higher, upwards of eight kilometres into the sky, it would later be explained, a narrow ribbon of wind was whipping across the northern hemisphere. This was a wild, chaotic thing, a thrumming bolt of electricity, a live python wriggling in a trap, a cracked whip, stinging. It howled far above glistening ice caps, arctic seas and glowing cities, racing itself to its own beginning, an endless loop. There was no slowing this wind, not now, not ever; it was the kind of unstoppable force that never ceases, merely changes direction. But as it reached the east coast of the United States it jumped into a screeching turn, swerving away from the thick, pressurised air above Bermuda. From there, it surged into the spiralling system just below Iceland, which, spinning round in the opposite direction, drove the wind harder and faster eastwards. The overall effect of the high- and low-pressure systems was to make the wind leaner, crueller, more determined. It tore onwards, without purpose, without shame.

* * *

The bed was not Pete's. He was clear about this.

'It's been sitting in my barn for years – was there when we moved in,' he said, as they looked at it, in the back of the van. The frame was dusty, streaked with cobwebs. The upholstered headboard was worn to threads.

'And the previous owners...?' said Vince, trailing off.

Vince had come out to the front garden in nylon shorts and rubber slides. He was still clutching the scourer, which was made from recycled hemp.

'Never actually met them,' said Pete, smiling, warmly. 'Couldn't say, really.'

'Anyway,' said Aster, clapping his hands together, his smile fixed.

'If it's got four legs, and you can lie on it, it'll do us,' said Aster.

He laughed and patted Vince on the shoulder.

'Won't it?' he said.

'Well,' said Vince.

'Up to you,' Pete said, shrugging, and turning.

Vince watched as Pete climbed into the van, and Aster followed him. The two men gripped the bed frame, together.

'Anyway,' said Pete, from the depths of the van as Aster backed up, heaving his end, slowly, outwards. 'Bit of sanding, bit of staining, it'll be as good as new.'

'Exactly,' said Aster.

He reached the van's rear opening and looked down at Vince –

'Sorry, can you?'

– before lowering his end of the bedframe down into Vince's hands, guiding, then releasing it. Vince took the weight, and stumbled backwards slightly, caught off-balance.

'You got it?' said Pete, moving slowly towards him. 'Gently, now.'

Pete manoeuvred the bed past Aster, stepping down from the van with his end. Vince continued to walk his end backwards, watching Aster. Aster, still in the van, was looking at the mattress, which was leaning up against one side. He reached out to touch it, then nodded his head.

'This mattress doesn't look too bad, actually,' said Aster.

41

Pete, looking straight at Vince, raised one eyebrow.

'We'll probably dump the mattress,' said Vince.

Then, raising his voice: 'We'll dump it, Aster. Won't we?'

'I don't know,' said Aster, from the van, his voice a metallic echo. 'I mean, there are no obvious stains.'

'He's kidding,' Vince said. 'We'll get a new one.'

'I'm not kidding,' said Aster.

'He is,' said Vince.

'I'm not,' said Aster.

The bed frame wasn't all that heavy, once Vince got used to it, but it was wide, and awkward. Even with Pete's help, he had trouble carrying it through the house's narrow corridors. He went first, shuffling backwards through the front door and along the hallway, watching Pete, at the other end of the bed frame, as his eyes swept across the cracked tiles underfoot, the damp splotched walls, the rotting beams, above.

'Bit of a project, then,' said Pete, inhaling sharply.

Vince took a deep breath, then sighed it out.

They eased the bed round one corner, then another, gouging two chunks from the plastered walls before they reached the bedroom, or rather, what was going to be the bedroom. They had chosen this one to sleep in because there was only a single hole in the roof. They had covered it over with the lid from a takeaway box.

'That's that then,' said Pete. 'I suppose I better go and help.'

Vince said nothing.

'With the mattress, I mean,' said Pete.

Vince didn't respond.

'OK then,' said Pete.

When he was gone, Vince walked back to the kitchen, where there was still a sink full of washing up, because they didn't have a dishwasher, and never would, unless one was going spare, somewhere. He set about the dishes and listened to the two of them, outside, grunting and chuckling, as they brought in the old mattress. He tried not to think about it, and stayed at the sink, until the deed was done. Only when Pete was back in his van, did he go back outside, to say goodbye. The van backed towards them, then took a sharp right, and juddered as it hit the mud track again. He and Aster stood side by side, watching it go.

'There are limits to this,' said Vince. 'To how sorry I am.'

'Oh relax. It's just a mattress,' said Aster, waving, smiling.

'It's unhygienic,' said Vince. 'It's had other people all over it.'

'Absolutely,' said Aster, still smiling. 'Just like you.'

A breath is a motion is the air rising is water flowing

* * *

There was so much happening, so far above, way beyond most people's comprehension. Once it was all explained, it was troubling to think of all these motions, these invisible waves, these shifting whorls of heat and chill. It's all caused by warming seas and melting ice, it would be explained, calmly and considerately, by those who understood it, and stared daily into the face of it, and, somehow, continued to go on living their lives, regardless. Fortunately, it is only very occasionally, even now, it would be explained, that the ribbon of wind and the circle of spinning clouds, and the giant oval of high pressure take this specific and ill-fated position. It's only then, at times like these – this would be part of the explanation – that the particular vibrations caused by all this commotion have an agitating effect on the drifting moisture, further down. The result of all this was dark clouds, gathering in the sky, but it wouldn't be right to pin everything on them. Really, they had just been swept along by things – what else could they do? They had been dragged from where they were formed, far out at sea, and buffeted and compacted until all they became one seething mass, and then, the only place they could go was where the wind ribbon was going, and the only fate left to the mass, and to the doomed landscape below it, was the fate that was then unleashed, all at once, like an act of retribution.

* * *

It was up to them to save it all, but nothing could be saved. The rain had come, come harder than ever, and the river had broken its banks, and brown water was washing over everything, churning the muddy path to evil-smelling foam, crashing against the walls of the house, seeping in through every uncovered crevice. In the front garden, waist deep in it, in his boxer shorts, Vince felt hollowed out, featherlight, his legs shaking beneath him, his headache pulsing through his entire body. He had not slept, not really, not with that rain, not on that bed. It had been more of a half-sleep, a drawn-out night terror, a prolonged sensation of suffocating and resurfacing. Dawn was where it got worse, when he felt the water lapping at his throat. Dawn was when he had blinked, and sat up, and seen. And now they were out there, both of them, watching it all, rushing away from them.

'Are you going to help?' said Aster, a few metres off. He was wearing pyjamas, and wrestling with a tarpaulin, which had come loose, and been set adrift, and was now wrapping itself around him.

'I think we might have lost the cold frame,' said Vince, as the old window sped past him.

'Just save what you can,' said Aster. Then, 'Grab those wheels!'

'What?'

Vince turned to look, but his body seemed to be going in slow motion. Under his toes, the soil dissolved and shifted. He saw one bicycle wheel, and reached. His fingertips brushed it, but it got away.

'Fuck's sake,' said Aster. 'What are you doing?'

But Vince wasn't paying attention, because other things were sailing past, now. A tree branch, a bird's nest. A sofa cushion. A microwave. He looked beyond them, back to the main road, back towards the village. All he could see was water, reflection, everything moving, everything changing.

'Vince,' said Aster.

Vince turned, slowly, turned back to face the house, to face the water, rushing through it, pooling around it, eating away at it, a little hope rising in his heart. But the house was so full of holes it put up little resistance. The water flowed through it, in through its windows, out through its doors, passing through. It was already so ruined. Nothing more could happen to it.

'Vince!' said Aster.

He spun back. Aster was panting. He had managed to bundle the tarpaulin into an irregular armful, which he had lifted up, above his head. He was soaking wet, his hair plastered to his forehead, and he was trying to wade towards the house. But the current was too strong. He was barely moving.

'Can you... please... help?' said Aster.

Vince blinked. More stuff was coming. A footstool. A keyboard. He watched, in awe. And then he saw it, glistening, a flash of light, floating on the surface. He set out instantly, towards it.

'Vince!' said Aster. 'Where are you going?'

Vince paddled with his hands. He pushed with his legs. The mud sucked at his ankles. Hidden objects scratched at his shins. The flash, like a fragment of sunlight, was dancing on top of the water, hopping towards him, tearing away, teasing, beckoning. He saw he would never get it unless he went for it, right then. He took a deep breath. He jumped. He felt the water close over his head. He kicked and scraped and winced, and then his feet were free, and he was gliding forwards. He opened his eyes, blinked through grit, looked up towards the surface, searching, saw the flash once more. He forgot where he was for a second, opened his mouth to yell in excitement, and then the water was down his throat, and in his nostrils, and he was choking, and kicking himself to the surface. As he broke through, back into the morning, coughing, spluttering, the air rushing in, filling his chest, his outstretched hand found what he was looking for, and his fingers closed around the shiny foil packet.

'What the hell,' said Aster. 'What is it?'

Vince gasped, and coughed, coughed up water, all the air in his lungs. He took a deep breath, and, turning, triumphant, held it aloft, held it up to the sun, and said:

'I think this is it.'

Then:

'I think this is mine.'

CAIT ATHERTON

Looking for Light in the *Cingulate Cortex*

A pittering of applause lifts Druim from his seat, dram of amber *Talisker* in hand. He glances back at Kate as if searching for reassurance and she frowns, fearing he might sink down again. Fortunately, he's urged on by the diminutive father-of-the-bride with his preppy glasses and finger-in-the-socket frizz of hair who frisks his guests into full-blown clapping. *Druim Darach: The Viking Poet.* A couple of whistles. As Druim passes, the man bows in appreciation. *Why do these people love everything Scottish,* Kate wonders. *And that over-sized tartan dickey-bow is frankly ridiculous.* Druim's kilt swings as he negotiates the chicane between the Christmas tree and an urn of white roses then steps up to the small stage. It wobbles under his bulk. *The Starlight Ballroom, Waldorf Astoria, New York.* Kate allows herself a smile. *Not too shabby.*

From behind the thicket of white branches, Druim blinks.

For God's sake, concentrate! Kate stabs at him in their homespun sign language. *Find the white spot. And careful with that whisky!*

Each branch has been dipped in silver and hung with crystal snowflakes shedding multitudes of rainbows, reflected *ad infinitum* in the candle-lit mirrors. *From Tiffany's,* the bride's mother had informed Kate when she'd fingered a particularly beautiful prism at the rehearsal. *Do be careful.* Kate has to admit it's like an upmarket Narnia in here. Each huge window is swathed in fathoms of ice-blue silk shot with frost-grey, each chair covered in the same sumptuous fabric, tied at the back in a huge bow. The entire room shimmers with expense.

If Druim and I ever tie the knot it will be a pie and a pint in the Hackney Horseshoe afterwards, Kate decides. She is surprised at herself. *After all these years of turning him down, am I seriously considering saying yes?*

Druim scours the floorboards, searching for the dot on which he has been instructed to stand. He knocks against a branch and rainbows judder. As he shuffles out a small arc, a snowflake spears his forehead. He swats it away, crystals tinkling like falling dominoes.

Clumsy! Kate frowns.

And you need to cut down on the pizza, she notes. Not that Druim is fat, although recently Kate has noticed a slackness around his jowls. It's more that he's a tree-trunk of a man and everyone in this room is so, well, *toned*. Druim takes a nip of whisky. She makes a *verboten* sign, crossing her index fingers. *Go easy! The whisky's just a prop.* She guesses at this point he must feel like Elton John, trotting out *'Candle in The Wind'* or some other old crowd-pleaser for the umpteenth time.

He squints in her direction. She nods. *Start. And do a good job for God's sake. They're paying us a fortune for this.*

New York. Kate is still incredulous. Such a long journey and such ludicrous expense for an engagement party. Druim's agent had assured them that the bride's family could well afford it however. Physicians to the elite, they were known for their ultra-private clinic, just off Lexington Avenue. Indistinguishable from neighbouring Art Deco mansions, the clinic was said to be a pusher of boundaries, both medical and ethical. A quick *google* and Kate discovered that there you could be re-invigorated by blood transfusions harvested from Olympian athletes or inseminated using bona-fide Ivy-league sperm. Rumour also had it that it was the place to go if a celebrity needed a face-lift (or an anything-lift) as for maximum privacy there was reputed to be a secret tunnel leading directly to the Waldorf Astoria itself.

Back in their terraced house in Hackney she'd snorted into her cornflakes when she'd opened the actual invitation. *A recreation of Vogue Magazine, December 1929. Please dress accordingly.* Now however, sipping her glass of *Charlemagne Grand Cru*, she admits its ninety-year old pages really do seem to have reincarnated. Kitten-lashed women in beaded flapper dresses mingle, postures perfect from glossy bobs to chic heels, wrists poised to display cigarettes in holders. *Holders! Health-freak types,* she sniffs, desperate for a smoke herself. *None of these ciggies are lit.* The men are slick-quiffed Errol Flynns in cummerbund-waisted tuxedos, many sitting with their chins resting on brass-knobbed walking canes, a few sporting monocles. *Ridiculous.* And all guests swathed alike in ice white or frosty-blue, as if other colours have been banned from the room creating a weird invisibility when they pass by the curtains.

My elfin girl and I, here we lie under our silverlit tree…

Druim cranks up *Silverlit* with practiced Gaelic lilt. All these years living in London means Kate has to remind him to roll his r's with a bit more gruffness. *Off to a good start,* she decides, her shoulders relaxing. *And the fact he's blushing adds authenticity.* Kate notices the bride-to-be's mother biting her forefinger to mute a groan of pleasure. *Romantic words from a roughshod man. Gets them every time.* She knows he must look like he's from another planet: unkempt coppery hair in its trademark ponytail, huge freckled forearms, bear-like stance. His kilt, moss green and highland heather, had set them back badly a few years ago when they could least afford it, but God knows it was a good investment. Even those guests needing to refer discreetly to the printed words seem enchanted. *Like taking candy from children.* Then Kate feels a little mean. Who could have predicted this... *this fame?* A passing waiter refills her glass. She has to admit, it opens up all sorts of possibilities. A chill North Uist wave of guilt crashes over her. A gulp of champagne and the wave subsides into its restless winter ocean.

Her Skye-ward eyes look for The Lights, but I dare hope she'll look for me...

Kate feels the inevitable strafe of glances. *Here we go again. Getting a good look at my Skye-ward eyes?* And she wishes now that she'd worn something less, well, *black.* She hadn't banked on everyone following the Vogue instruction quite so religiously and she'd assumed that a trouser-suit would make her look intellectual, as befits a poet's partner. With a glint, a pair of spectacles swivel in her direction. It's the bride's father again. He's staring. *Hey! I know the poem is about me. But it was written 25 years ago! Do you expect me to have been in cryogenic suspension?* She frowns and looks away.

But if she's honest, the same thought has occurred to her. When she'd joked to Druim recently that her looks were turning more gnomic than elfin, his mouth had drooped, puzzled, then hurt. *Come on!* She'd given him a little push. *You take it all so bloody seriously Druim. Like we were still the kids in the poem, lying on that freezing beach.*

Kate fluffs her greying hair, aware the man is still watching. She tries not to cringe at the poem's over-familiar words. *Bloody uncomfortable,* she thinks. *To have the moment your boyfriend lost his virginity immortalised for the world to gawp at.* But she forces up the corners of her mouth, sensing that it is not advisable to look too churlish. *After all, Silverlit pays.* She remembers, just a few years ago, how hopeless things had seemed. Druim's teaching cut right back and her losing overtime at the estate agency, it seemed they'd never pay off their mortgage. But now that's done she can plan improvements to their Victorian terrace. Tonight alone will cover a new master ensuite. Then she'd like an extension to the kitchen, bifold doors, lantern roof, the lot. *Will be worth a small fortune.*

I never thought Druim would make us so rich.
   Another icy wave of guilt.
   Ask me again Druim... and I might say yes.

Druim ploughs on and Kate reminds herself that normally she copes well enough with this *Silverlit* baloney. It's just the idiots who get her goat. Like that horsey-maned journalist from The Sunday Telegraph Magazine, Clarissa (or was it Claudia) who'd brayed: 'How does it feel to have the world's favourite contemporary love poem written about one? Are you our modern-day Helen of Troy?'
   Kate had shrugged. *To me, Silverlit is a joke. Quite literally.* Of course, she didn't say that out loud. *The game would be up.* But taking Kate's silence as a snub the journalist had sipped her coffee like Kate had spiked it with battery acid.

We lie under the vaulted sky, and free...
We fall together, starfire in her shaken hair
Melt-melding. Me into she into me.

Kate marvels yet again at how Druim somehow makes the last lines scan. And how he keeps the emotion up too. By the last line, his voice actually trembles. After a climactic pause allowing the room to collectively breathe again, he remembers his instructions. He turns and raises his glass. All eyes lift as a curtain sweeps back and above the stage the bride-to-be is revealed, posed on a balcony. Her dress is copied exactly from Vogue's front cover. Snow-white cloche hat, polar-bear fur collar plunging to her navel, the inner slopes of her breasts barely covered with fluff. Tiers of pearls. A miniature Christmas tree in each hand. Her impressive cleavage is the one departure permitted from the original 1929 model. Kate raises an eyebrow. *Have the family operating theatres been beavering away?* She realises that the bride-to-be's father is still staring and flushes at the thought of him reading her mind. Tipping over the rail, the young woman opens her palms and releases a sweep of glitter which winks downwards to the stage.
   Druim flicks glitter out of his hair. Blinks. Just then a side-door is punched open and an ear-splitting drone vibrates ribcages and *Tiffany* crystal alike. With a toss of shaggy bearskin a piper strides in, full Highland dress, elbow squeezing hard on the bag. A flurry of piercing notes. Guests gasp. The groom rises from his seat, grabs an armful of white roses and mounts the balcony stairs, two at a time.
   I'll take the High Road? Kate wonders. *Very droll.* After allowing their guests sufficient time to switch their phone cameras to video mode, the

couple kiss. The piper segues into *Should Auld Acquaintance Be Forgot* and everyone rises to their feet, arms linked, champagne glasses raised. The iceberg of a diamond on the bride-to-be's finger flashes with triumphant semaphore.

Kate grits her teeth. *What a piece of kitsch.* She mouths to Druim: *Thank God it's over! Let's have a laugh about this over a beer.* But he's mobbed by young women framing selfies and asking him to sign his book. Kate sighs. *Part of the deal.* His sporran has gone a little skew-whiff. She decides to straighten it out.

As Kate makes her way towards the stage she's tasered by a smile from the bride-to-be's glamourous mother. At the rehearsal Kate had mistaken her for an older sister to the bride, the memory of this makes her reach for her hair again. *Is it so hard to believe this mop was once full of fallen stars?* The woman smiles sympathetically. *Too sympathetically.* She steps between Kate and the stage, her cigarette holder held up like a barrier. Kate's blood sours.

I get it. Right now, Druim belongs to your daughter.

Accepting a fresh glass of champagne, Kate sees the bride-to-be join Druim under the branches. She snuggles so close he's forced to drape an arm around her slim shoulders, she raises her lovely face and Druim's cheeks blush with something Kate can't quite identify at this distance. *Embarrassment, surely?*

Kate empties her glass and signals for a refill. *I need a cigarette. A real one.* A little unsteady on her feet, she makes her way to the back of the room. The French doors open with one firm twist of the knob.

'Oh. She of the starfire hair...'

It's a parody of Druim's accent but not a cruel one. In the chill darkness she identifies the speaker immediately by the fuzz of hair, silhouette of bow-tie around his neck. Like a stage magician, he produces a light for her, holds it steady until her cigarette glows:

'Good evening. I'm Professor Wilf. Proud father of the bride. And a specialist in the Neuro-imaging of Love.'

Kate snorts and a bubble of champagne inflates from her nostril. She sniffs it back.

'Neuro-imaging of Love. Really?'

His politeness is undeterred.

'Correct, ma'am. Sabbatical in your fair city of Edinburgh as a student, so I consider myself a little *Scot-teesh*, if I may say so. Our wonderful Viking Poet certainly lit up our *cingulate cortices* tonight.'

Kate glances at the sky, assuming he is referring to some faint rash of stars. Most have been doused by Manhattan's blazing skyscrapers, Christmas billboards, rivers of headlights.

'No,' he corrects her, tapping his head. 'In here. Between the *amygdala* and the *nucleus acumbens*. Precisely patterned neuronal activity in the brain's *cingulate cortex*. The signature of true love.'

Kate forces her eyes not to roll. He continues:

'Not to be confused with mere lust of course. Oh no. What I am talking about is *pure* love, one human being for another. Until now we have had to guess what our lovers felt about us. Simply believe what they told us. But now we can detect the truth. A breakthrough, if I say so myself.'

He reaches into a pocket and pulls out what looks like a *Star Trek* map, holds it up in the meagre light. Cauliflower-like contours are over-lit with galaxies of magenta, emerald, tangerine.

'The brain's night sky,' he declares. 'An internal Aurora Borealis.' He points out a small supernova, an explosion of intense silver.

'We had the bridegroom thoroughly analysed, of course.'

'Really?'

His magnified eyes are trained on her face.

'My dear. No-one can be too careful when it comes to love. Fortunately, he passed his pre-nuptial scan with flying colours. Here is his *cingulate cortex*, beautifully lit up.'

Kate inhales the merciful nicotine.

'Look,' she ventures. 'I don't want to be rude, but maybe he was thinking of someone else when his brain lit up? Some other girl? Boy, even.'

'Excellent question. But rest assured, we know what we are doing. The subject enters our magnetic resonance scanner and is shown random images of attractive people.' He snaps his fingers: 'Click, click, click. Like this, but faster. Hundreds. Occasionally, we insert an image of the beloved. The *possible* beloved, I should say. It happens too rapidly for the conscious mind to evaluate. And the brain cannot lie. The computer analyses the emotional response to the beloved's image. Impossible to fake. The very deepest feelings revealed.'

They both fall silent.

'Look,' he says. 'Our Viking Poet captured the very essence of love. I believe those words came only from the purest source.'

Kate puts a hand out to steady herself.

The professor straightens his bow-tie, opens the door. Pauses:

'My dear, do excuse me. I have a proposal to put to him.'

* * *

'I can't believe you agreed to it!'

Kate and Druim sit amidst the choreographed bustle of a Waldorf Astoria breakfast. A waiter pours coffee from a silver teapot then with theatrical flourish tongs flaky croissants from a basket. Kate nudges Druim:

'Use your napkin. And I can't believe you agreed to it!'

Outside the traffic surges nose-to-bumper, tiny commuters barrel along the sidewalks. Their faraway existence is hushed by thick carpets and brocaded curtains, leaving only the clink of china and hiss of cappuccino steam.

Kate prods Druim's thigh, hard.

'I said I can't believe you agreed. The mad professor wants you to recite *Silverlit*? In his MRI machine? How will that prove anything?'

Druim rubs his leg.

'Look Kate, he's invented a new discipline. *Neuro-literary Imaging.* Wants to show how poetry evokes specific brain states and write the very first paper on it. Just imagine? *Silverlit* appearing in the science textbooks… What an amazing thought!'

But still the idea rattles her. *Silverlit is about me after all.* Revealing what's in Druim's mind when he recites it will be yet another invasion of her privacy.

And what if nothing lights up for him?

She watches him as he chews. *That secret sky of his brain…* But he had never let her down, had he? Surely she has nothing to fear?

Of course it will explode with colour for me.

What Kate herself remembers most about the *Silverlit* night was that it had hurt. Partly *down there* of course, but more painful was the embarrassment that she'd actually allowed it to happen. Technically they were just friends at the time, flat-mates in that student dump in the Holloway Road. He'd invited her up to North Uist for a proper *Hogmanay*, she'd never even been to Scotland before, let alone a god-forsaken, windy rock. He wasn't her type, but he intrigued her. This huge guy who could so easily have swiped the living daylights out of snarky city boys when they teased him about his accent, his hair, his politeness… but instead he would just pucker his sandy eyebrows, as if trying to puzzle out what response would help him best fit in. She had never met a man so physically strong, yet so gentle.

Weak or gentle? All these years later and I still don't really know.

At the time she had expected her on-off Italian boyfriend to invite her to Rome for Christmas. But the bastard had gone ski-ing without her. And, for some reason, she had always longed to see the Northern Lights.

'We're going to look for the Northern Lights.' That's what they'd said when they'd left his parents, hand-in-hand on their bungalow's sofa, chuckling at an episode of Fawlty Towers.

'You'll be lucky,' replied his dad with a wink.

She remembered how the salty blast had scoured her lungs. Released from the bungalow's tinselly fug they'd sand-waded across the dunes, the winter sea heaving and collapsing in darkness beyond. She'd steadied herself against him, giddy with whisky slugged from the bottle he'd picked up on their way out. Then she'd tripped and together they collapsed under a gale-twisted tree, laughing about something, something hilarious she wishes she could remember, but can't. *Why wasn't that in the poem, whatever it was? A bit of humour?* There they'd lain, staring at the sky. She had forced herself not to blink, didn't want to miss her chance to see The Lights. She continued to stare, even when his mouth unexpectedly weighted itself on hers. She could have stopped him, she should have stopped him... she could never understand why she hadn't. And of course, it had hurt. Not the obvious, but a twig got down the back of her jeans. She had stared at the sky, willing colour to ignite the dark vault above. But she was torn from her sky-gazing by the shock of it, then a riddling warmth. Yes, true, there had also been snow, but just a smattering; a rarity apparently, so close to the sea. Possibly some really had fallen into her hair, that she couldn't say.

But the endless vault remained unlit. I didn't see the Northern Lights. Never did.

She'd sworn then and there that there wouldn't be a second time. The next day she'd avoided his glances, kept her distance whilst washing-up at the sink and prised her hand from his shy, freckled fingers. On their journey back to London she had stood alone on the ferry deck, claiming she felt sea-sick. But the train from Inverness was overbooked, forcing them to sit on their suitcases. Somewhere near Berwick-upon-Tweed she'd fallen asleep, then been jolted awake to find her head on his shoulder, huge arm looped around her.

Back in their flat, they had drifted into coupledom: *Kate and Dave. Economics and English Literature.* Like magnets, she found it easier to just let it happen. It wasn't unpleasant, in fact there was a force field around him that made her feel oddly protected. They dreamt, but separately: she of starting her own business, becoming wealthy; he, he once confided, of becoming a poet.

Within a year the Italian came back with a riot of parties, drugs and expensive dinners. Then he'd buggered off home, leaving only a phone number that was answered by a woman who refused to speak English. At first Dave was brooding, resentful even, but he was there to lean against during the worst of it and once again his magnet worked its invisible forces. Without discussion, their relationship took up where it had left off.

He'd asked her to marry him but she'd laughed and said why bother? All that expense for a piece of paper.

And years later, whilst clearing out their flat, she'd found *Silverlit*. Scribbled on an old train ticket, dimmed by dust at the back of his desk, a relic of that long-ago *Hogmanay*. Giggling, she'd showed it to him. It was so unbelievably corny. She said she would throw it away and he agreed but hoping to continue the fun with a hilarious rejection, she submitted it to the University poetry anthology instead. To improve the joke, she had the brainwave that *Dave* should become *Druim*.

Both were blind-sided when it was published and won a prize.

'Enchanting,' one reviewer had said. 'A Scottish Dylan Thomas,' opined another. Wishing to cite this sole success in his interview for teacher training college, it seemed sensible to change his name officially to *Druim*. One thing led to another. *Silverlit* appeared in *Best New Poems of 1991* and even got an airing on *Poetry Please*. The request was from Druim's mum, which embarrassed Kate to her toenails. Then, naturally, nothing. Inevitable obscurity.

But *Silverlit's* light had not gone out. One Friday night, about three years ago, dozing in the *Screen on the Green* after yet another enervating week selling rabbit hutches to overpaid City boys, Kate poked Druim awake. Set way back in the early nineties, the arty film featured star-crossed male lovers spending Christmas in their snow-blasted Highland croft. A sense of familiarity dawned over Kate. *The older lover was reading Silverlit to the younger!* It took a moment to truly sink in, Kate mentally checked off the words as they emerged: *Yes! Yes! Yes!* With glee they remained in their seats until the late-night repeat, then they returned to witness the miracle a dozen times more. Kate pointed out her growing concern that the poem was being used ironically, but Druim remained rapt.

Suddenly, whenever a couple planned a winter wedding but felt themselves too hip for a Shakespearean Sonnet, *Silverlit* was declaimed. But it was in America that it truly took off.

'The romance of fornicating on a frosty beach,' was how Druim's enthusiastic new agent so crudely put it. A lavishly illustrated edition was quickly produced, bulked up with some of Druim's lesser poems. The agent also filed a legal case to claim back royalties from the film. *Silverlit* quickly sold out in the States. The Americans preferred it read aloud in its native Scottish lilt – and the rich were prepared to pay for the thrill. Kate and Druim were stunned as the invitations rolled in. First Palm Beach, then Los Angeles – now New York.

Silverlit might belong to her dim past, Kate told herself. But it was blazing out a new future.

One afternoon, just back from Los Angeles with Druim teaching, Kate had bought her boss home. They had been valuing a neighbouring property and she wanted his advice. He poked around the back yard, agreed it was big enough for an extension, inspected the plans for the master ensuite and confirmed the likely profit margin. In fact, he confirmed far more than she'd dared hope. Pulling her onto her bed he confirmed she was still attractive. The only excuse she could find was that it was so unlike her to feel excitement about anything, a moment of madness. It was as she took a shower before going back to work that the icy North Uist wave first broke:

Poor Druim. Kate had shivered. *I can't leave him now. Not with things going so well.*

But in the months to come, she found it increasingly easy to blame Druim. *We never laugh anymore. He is so sensitive! No fun.* And any criticism that *Silverlit* received in the press felled him like an axe-blow. After Claudia from the Sunday Telegraph Magazine had deemed the poem 'a tad hackneyed' Kate had to take him to his GP to be prescribed anti-depressants.

'Ignore her Druim, just an envious bitch,' Kate had said. 'But remember, *Silverlit* was only published in the first place for a laugh! Don't take it to heart.'

Strangely, after that he became even more withdrawn.

A waiter informs them that the clinic's limousine has arrived. Kate tugs at Druim's sleeve.

'Forget the stupid clinic. Let's go up the Empire State Building? Or see where John Lennon was shot? A bit of Christmas shopping? Anything other than spending our last morning in a bloody clinic.'

Druim's brow puckers. For a moment he looks tempted.

His phone vibrates, twists on the table. He squints at the message.

'Oh. The case has been decided. Agent confirms the royalties for the film will be back-dated.'

Kate's spirits soar. *Thousands upon thousands! Maybe it really is time they got married?* Perhaps he could be persuaded to propose again on top of the Empire State Building? She takes Druim's arm:

'That settles it. Let's have some fun!'

He nips his lip. Then he speaks, concerned, as if she's forgotten something important:

'No. We *have* to do this, Kate. Especially now.'

Kate follows Druim into the limousine. The vehicle is cavernous with a gilt-mirrored cocktail bar and wrap-around TV. They sit, awkward amidst such over-the-top luxury.

So, what will we see in the sky of your brain Druim? She's surprised at herself for feeling worried.

Will there still be light in there for me?

'Stop!' Kate points to a passing department store, wondering if they have a jewelry department. 'Forget the stupid test, Druim. Let's stop here!'

But he's picking a nail, deep in thought.

More like a hotel than a clinic, at the top of curved steps they are welcomed by a saluting doorman standing under a copper awning. They circle through the revolving door out onto vanilla marble tiles, a chandelier hanging from the ceiling, paneled walls. Sounds echo with the detachment peculiar to such sparse elegance: a murmur from the reception desk, a wisp of violin concerto from the waiting room. The faraway bleep of a machine.

Druim returns from the desk, voice awed to a whisper:

'The Department for the Neuro-imaging of Love. They're expecting us now.'

Emerging from the lift they are greeted and asked to take a seat. On the far side of the room a heavy door slides open, revealing the pristine maw of an MRI machine. It yawns like an open throat. The thought of being swallowed whilst its all-seeing eye scours for hidden secrets makes Kate shiver.

Rather you than me, Druim. Serve you right for agreeing to this.

An older woman emerges from the scanning room, back-combed ash-blonde hair, crimson lipstick, matching handbag and heels. A man has his arm around her waist. *Holding her up or claiming possession?* Kate wonders. *Both*, she concludes, noticing that he is at least a decade younger. They sit and the woman rests her lacquered nails on the man's chest. She stares at Kate defiantly. Kate blushes and reaches for Druim's hand, seeking that magnetic reassurance. He's still lost in thought. The receptionist purrs, the couple rise and enter the consulting room.

'Getting their results, I expect,' Kate remarks. 'You'll be next for the torture chamber, Druim.'

Druim tears a thumbnail between his teeth.

56

After about ten minutes the couple emerge. The woman's lips have thinned, she grasps a sheaf of papers. The man trails behind, scowling. With the clamp of the lift doors, they disappear.

Druim gets up to follow them.

'Let's go.'

'Nervous Druim?' Kate raises an eyebrow. 'You should have listened to me in the first place.'

'Good morning!' Professor Wilf materialises between them and the lift. 'Welcome to the Neuro-imaging of Love.' He claps his hands together. 'What an honour. The world's most romantic living poet is with us.'

The receptionist holds up a camera and takes a picture of Druim.

'Tell him we're leaving,' Kate hisses to Druim under her breath.

The professor swings round, looks at her.

'Oh, she of the shaken hair...'

What is it about him? Kate thinks. *It's as if he's absorbed the penetrating vision of his damn machine and sees inside my skull.*

The professor blinks.

'Right now my dear, the one in whom we're interested is you.'

Kate grimaces. *Has this little man lost his marbles?*

'Oh, it's clear how our poet feels about you, anyone can sense that without hi-tech machinery. But you're the mystery. To be the recipient of such beautiful sentiments, but are they reciprocated? That's what fascinates us.'

The professor glances at Druim, who assents with a tiny nod.

'He agrees with me, like any partner, he has the right to know. Remove necklace, rings, any other metal objects. Come this way. Everything is ready.'

Kate grabs Druim's arm.

'You can't do this to me!'

But Druim twists, forcing her hand to drop. She gasps like she's been shoved into a perishing winter ocean. The professor grips her elbow, guides her into the room.

Seconds after being slid into the scanner, images flash onto her eyeballs. Attractive people of all types. Waving, smiling. She glimpses Druim's face and is flooded by icy panic.

Somewhere close-by, Druim is reciting *Silverlit* like a prayer. She lies, scanned, measured, assayed. Searches, searches... but still the sky remains unlit.

The machine stops just as Druim finishes. She wants to reach for him but knows there is no point.

She doesn't see the Northern Lights. Never did.

Mission Accomplished

I got Yas off three times the night we started bombing Iraq. I didn't know what else to do and I guess she didn't either. We'd gone to the protests a few weeks before, marching with a Schuyler contingent even though Yas had nothing to do with the college, but that worldwide movement — we'd seen pictures from everywhere, from Canada to South Africa — hadn't stopped the bombs we'd watched explode in the darkness, across oceans and continents. Yas started crying when she came down, buried her face against my collarbone, and said something that sounded like 'Stop …' She fell asleep with her arm belting my stomach, face hidden, strands of hair mussed against the hair in my armpit.

I don't know when I fell asleep. The room seemed abnormally dark, even for a garden apartment like ours, which in western New York winter is just a basement. Even the thin light that normally spilled from the tiny yard was gone. I stared into the dark ceiling, willing images of bombs to stop exploding against it. I woke with Yas turned away from me, too far to spoon, holding the cow-print pillow to her chest. She jumped when I put my hand at her nape, but not as if I had woken her.

'Is it late?' she asked.

'I don't know.' Both of us still refused to get cellphones, Yas because of her electrical-engineer father's paranoia about surveillance, me because it just seemed too demanding. I didn't like anyone to place demands on me but Yas. We had an old-fashioned digital clock on our nightstand, the kind with flipping numbers. It had been my aunt's. Yas liked it because it reminded her of *Groundhog Day*, the first movie she had watched on TV when she arrived in the US. I leaned over Yas to see it. '8:12.'

'I'm gonna be late.' Her voice was flat.

'Call in.'

'I don't want to talk to people.'

'I'll call in for you.'

'They don't know about you.'

'I'll pretend I'm you.'

I did; my mimicry wasn't bad. Yas watched me for a second, then rolled over as I heard someone answer the phone. The lab supervisor, Gina, said, 'Oh, of *course*,' with a kind of theatrical understanding. I tried to imitate

Gina's tone to Yas, but I felt like a five-year-old telling a grown-up joke, trying to get a laugh from something I wasn't really in on. Yas didn't laugh, anyway. She studied my ear, said, 'Yeah, she's like that,' and brushed my arm lightly with her nails as she walked towards the bathroom.

Schuyler was still on spring break, so I didn't have to work either. While Yas was in the shower, I made an omelet with olives, parsley, and feta cheese and looked at the *Buffalo News*, the *Chicago Tribune*, and the *Washington Post* on my laptop, swallowing sickness at images of bombs hitting the Presidential Palace, soldiers making the incursion into Basra. They were filed, according to their captions, only a few hours before. Sometimes I was still amazed by the Internet, everything both immediate and far away.

I didn't notice Yas coming to stand beside me, one green towel knotted at her chest and another around her hair. She flipped the laptop shut and said, holding up the plated omelet, 'Is it okay if I take this back to bed?'

I shrugged, nodded. I watched her back, a few wet strands of hair escaping the second towel. I wanted to reach for Yas, to open a palm between her shoulder blades as if it would comfort her, provide some protection. She closed the door behind her.

Yas and I met three weeks after September 11. Buffalo was just close to and far enough from New York City, and I was just close to and far enough from college, that by the beginning of October I was truly lost. Yas, sitting on a stool at Millie's, different in color and style from most of the patrons, seemed to know exactly where she was. Of course, it didn't hurt that she was so gorgeous as to emit light from bare, delicate shoulders. I don't know what she saw in me, and I've always been a little afraid to ask her, but our chemistry that night startled us both. I'd gone to Millie's planning to take someone home, to fuck out my weird, chaotic energy — four years of college had cultivated in me a deep appreciation for sex as forgetting—but I clung to Yas as if to a buoy in a crashing sea. Sweat had streaked her eyeliner, light gray trails running to jaw and ears. I had never seen anyone prettier, and I told her so.

'Shut up,' she said, running fingernails straight along my underwear line. I was no longer wearing underwear. Yas hadn't said anything about the ungroomed state I had allowed myself to get to, nor had she seemed to mind it. She had a substantial bush too, but hers was well-trimmed and shaped. She was straddling my thigh, surprisingly velvety.

'No, I mean it.'

'How many girls have you seen naked?'

If I thought the question was a little much for our first time, I didn't want her to know I thought that. 'Eight, including you.'

'And you're how old?'

'Twenty-one. Until next month.'

'You'll see someone prettier.'

'I don't want to see anyone prettier.'

'So you admit they exist.' She was leaning down, pecking my neck, my collarbone. Her nipples brushed mine. Her hand with its gentle, short fingernails had started to move inward, and she put her full weight on my leg when I squirmed.

'They might. But it's hard to imagine.'

'They do exist, I promise. They just don't fuck as good as me.' She pushed her finger in at the same time she said it, and I squealed. She laughed, tilting her head back, and I saw shadows on the roof of her mouth and clean, tiny teeth.

Neither of us had thought of ourselves as U-Hauling types, but within a month we were spending almost every night together. I hadn't lied to Yas, but I had been talking big: she was the first woman I had ever spent more than one night with. I had never had a girlfriend, never fallen in love before. Yas was actually the one to say it first, the word 'love' dark in the back of her throat, but I jumped to respond, as if she'd just introduced me to language. What surprised me was how physical it was to be in love with her. I don't mean sex; I mean that Yas, almost immediately, felt like part of my body. Her laughter elevated me, as if I were both comedian and audience. Once or twice I came just by making Yas come. When she told me about her high-school girlfriend, who had outed her to the school and her parents, I mirrored the stiffness in her shoulders, and I felt her start to cry before there was sound or tears. (Yas's father, always the gentle hand in the family, had sort of come around, but her mother had died before doing so, and Yas had never brought a girlfriend home; her tone made it clear I was by no means guaranteed to be the first.) While I couldn't say the new smells of living with someone—body odor from sweating under a quilt, the echoing funk when she'd just used the bathroom — were pleasant, they were familiar, almost mine. I came to know Yas's stories so well that I might have lived them.

I tried to explain these feelings to Yas, my girlfriend. My girlfriend. She snorted, reached down to cup me, and said, 'Yeah, so what you mean is, right now you're masturbating.' *Masturbating* was one of the words she had an accent on, that British-schooled accent opening and widening the letter *a*. That wasn't what I meant at all, but explaining further seemed hopeless, so I kissed her.

Yas's family had moved to the US when Yas was eleven; Yas, her parents, and her brother Gabir had gotten citizenship somehow through

Dr. Obeidi's work as an engineer and then an engineering professor. Yas's aunt in Iraq had been involved in some anti-Ba'ath Party activism for a couple of years when they departed. 'I don't *know*, Shan,' Yas had said impatiently when I pressed her for details. 'I was a kid. It was just better we got out.'

The family's English had been pretty good — Yas and her brothers went to a British-run school in Baghdad — but the sharp hallway ricochets of American English made junior high discomfiting for Yas. She'd found only one close friend, Dunia, who became her girlfriend when they were sophomores and then betrayed her. Even hearing Dunia's name made me tense, two streaks of fire down my back. Another Arab-American from a private, tentative family, she knew exactly how hard she was fucking Yas over by outing her.

I hadn't yet come out to my own mother, who was really my only family, when I met Yas. That left a choice between lying or taking about five new steps at once when Yas and I moved in together, and I chose the latter. My mother, always drawn to outsiders, processed it fairly well, but she and Yas never managed to get along. Mom seemed to expect Yas to be more like the Croatian and Bosnian teenage waitresses she'd been managing at Polly's Café since the mid-nineties, most of whom were — 'by nature,' according to my mother — hesitant and deferential to authority. Yas's irreverence appeared in any conversation within five minutes; it was one of my favorite things about her. Mom kept glancing at me when Yas made a sarcastic comment or even one that relied on sophisticated English, then quickly refocusing on Yas when I didn't try to mitigate her discomfort. When Yas and I talked about Mom after that first dinner, Yas just shrugged. 'It's a pretty normal kind of racism,' she said. 'Whatever. I've seen it before.' I was too upset to talk for several hours after she said 'racism,' even though I thought she might be right.

A day into the war and then another, I followed troop movements and bombings even though I'd never understood anything about the military, watched us secure petroleum fields ('of course,' Yas said), battle for Nasiriyah. I read headlines aloud after dinner; Yas sometimes got up in the middle and walked to the bedroom, short hair mussed to one side, but I couldn't stop myself. I scoured the papers as if they would offer something to do, something to change. About a week in, when I read something about a city called Kirkuk, Yas gasped and swallowed. I watched her throat jump, my mouth slightly open, waiting. 'Go on,' she said.

'What?'

'That's where my aunts are. My dad's sisters. Go on.'

61

I read the article, then another at her request. My voice was getting tired, but she wouldn't look at the screen, so I read a third. I sat with the computer on my lap, facing the coffee table and the front wall with its tiny, high windows; Yas was sideways on the couch, her toes tucked beneath my thigh. She shook me off when I reached for her foot while I was reading, but after I'd put the laptop on the coffee table, she let me cradle her heels in my hand. Her eyes were closed, green eyeshadow hastily brushed.

'Do you talk to them a lot?' I asked. 'Does your dad?'

Yas shook her head. 'I don't know. I don't know about my dad.'

'Do you remember them from when you were a kid?'

'That's not the point.'

I hadn't realized, until then, that there was a point. I put her feet down gently on my thigh. She frowned, turned, and reached for the slippers that her friend Lina had knitted for her, green and blue stripes.

'I used to go there all the time,' she said. 'When we were kids.'

The photographs with the articles weren't helping me picture it: bombs flashing in the night again, desertscapes with tents, soldiers in camo standing in front of blocky beige buildings. 'What was it like?'

'It was my aunties' houses. I don't know. My auntie Zeytun had these red tiles in her hallway and they were always cold, no matter how hot it was outside.' Yas shrugged, looking at our exposed brick wall.

'What does it look like? What were the people like?'

'There was this store around the corner that a husband and wife owned, and the husband made really good kleicha. They're like … I don't know. They're these swirly cookies, with dates in them. My auntie Naziha would take me and Gabir to get some every day. Mostafa and Basim would pretend they were too old to go until we got back and then they'd try to steal ours.' I'd never met either of Yas's oldest brothers; both of them had already been married by the time their parents decided to move, and they'd stayed behind in Baghdad. Basim and his family lived in Dubai now, but they'd never been to the States. Yas wasn't out to either of them, so they'd never heard of me.

'I mean, just like, what kind of a place is Kirkuk?'

Yas shrugged. 'If someone asked you what kind of a place Buffalo is, could you answer?'

'Kind of.'

'Go ahead.'

'You know, it's kind of a Rust Belt city but it's also … like it has this sense of history, you can feel what it was like in the Industrial Revolution …'

'Nothing you just said would mean anything to an Iraqi.' Yas raised an eyebrow, expanding the smoky green shade underneath. 'I mean, you know. An Iraqi who never lived here. Those aren't actually feelings. It's just hard to — you can't, not quite.' There was something final about her voice, the topic closed. She sat up. 'Also, I'm not gonna be home next Wednesday.'

'What's up?'

'We're having dinner. Rania's having a baby.'

'What? Oh my god!' I grinned, realizing how stiff my face had been. Rania, Gabir's wife, was a bubbly, round-cheeked pharmacist who had only worn vivid jewel-toned hijabs since September 11, and the only member of Yas's family who liked me without hesitation. 'We're gonna be aunts for real —'

I stopped abruptly, looking at my girlfriend. Yas shrugged and looked away.

My breath hissed between my teeth as I asked, 'Did they tell you I couldn't come?'

'It's just easier, Shan.'

'So it's not Rania and Gabir, it's just easier for you?'

'You know what Gabir's like.'

'Barely, because I barely see him.'

Yas shook her head hard, dark strands fluttering. 'Shan, seriously, not now.'

'When do I get to really know your family?' I asked, blinking.

'It's just not easy for me.'

That was what she always said about this subject, and I blinked as my frustration built behind my eyelids. 'I didn't say it was. But they're important to you, and I want to think I am too.'

'And I'm supposed to talk to them about it now?'

She was supposed to talk to them about it long before this, but I didn't say it. She watched the floor by my foot. I stood, grabbed a sponge, and started brushing crumbs from the kitchen counter.

I went to work every day, hating, deeply, that work was still work. Students with the same pointless anxieties, the same shallow grade-based complaints. I wanted to scream at them that my girlfriend was actually suffering, that for all she knew her aunties had just been killed or ousted from bombed-out homes. At least Schuyler College was full of anti-war posters (albeit defaced from time to time). They papered the hallway I walked every morning en route to my office. Also, a few sophomores — among them one of my advisees, Kayla Scharnhorst — had started a weekly sit-in at school a month before we dropped our first bombs; since March 20

63

they'd been there every Monday, Wednesday, and Friday. They huddled shoulder to shoulder in a semicircle outside the administration building, two floors below my office window, sheltering a few candles from the wind until campus security demanded they put them out. Often one or more students would give a speech through a megaphone detailing the war's most recent casualties, injustices that soldiers were inflicting; after each recitation, the group would intone, 'Not in our name!' Sometimes they sang, thin voices buoyed by the beautifully trained dark-chocolate bass of one broad, bearded white guy who was often the only man there.

I watched them day after day, sitting next to my window, opening it when the weather allowed; soon enough I started marking the time as busy, not taking appointments from noon until one-thirty or two, when the protest was usually over. A couple of weeks into April, shortly after Baghdad fell, I walked downstairs and stood watching the group for a while. Kayla caught my eye and smiled slightly, unable to change her face much during a song. A blonde strand fell over her left eyebrow. Buffalo being Buffalo, she and her companions were all still swathed in scarves and fleeces, but their wardrobe seemed more colorful than that of their fellow students — a magenta scarf, a pair of bright green boots. (Yas had a few things like that in her wardrobe — it heightened contrast, since she tended to wear a lot of black. I was a plain plaid-and-jeans type, or slacks-and-loafers for work; Yas said she liked that about me.) I backed up a little after the singing ended, when a young woman I didn't recognize took the megaphone out and started listing the deaths that week, what Dick Cheney didn't want us to know.

Two days later I took my lunch break right at noon and joined the half-circle, sliding in beside Kayla, whose small smile wrinkled with confusion. I knew a couple of the songs just from listening, but others were unfamiliar; since I'm not much of a singer, I let most go by, trying to absorb the music. I felt a current pass through us, we who stood with others against the bombardment. With the power in this circle I could protect Yas, from the fear for her aunts, the blank expression that solidified around her eyes whenever the news came on.

That night, Friday, Yas emerged from the bedroom, wearing the baby-blue silk shorty pajamas I'd bought her for Valentine's last year. She wiggled her Altoids tin between her fingers. I grinned and tucked the newspaper under the couch as she began rolling a joint beside me. I watched her tongue seal its edge and listened to the iridescent laugh that escaped her after her second hit and my third. I spread my arms wide, across the length of the couch, but nearly slammed them down when she kissed my armpit.

'That tickles!' I complained, laughing for a long, vibrating time.

'Does it feel good?'

'No, it tickles!'

'I think that's good.' She giggled, going for the same spot.

'I don't.' I jerked my arm back, but I was still laughing.

'Mmm,' said Yas, and she kissed at the V of my undershirt instead. I breathed to the spot. 'Better?'

'Mmm-hmm.' She let her head rest there. My chest seemed to open up beneath her cheek, the way that outside our high windows the night was presumably opening over the city. 'I miss you,' I murmured.

Even high I expected her to roll her eyes and say 'I live with you,' but instead she kissed my breast, barely moving her head, and said, 'I miss you too.'

'You do?'

'So much. I ...' She tried to lift herself from my chest, but all I could see was her crown, the part in her shiny hair. 'I love you. Just hard for me.' Her head settled back down. I could feel the outline of her ear. I thought about the senses, how weird it was that we thought of touch as existing only in our fingertips. Really it was everywhere. You could feel things everywhere. Yas kept speaking, into my skin. 'Hard for us. Yeah? I love you, Shan.' She said it like a discovery, like she hadn't just said it a few minutes before. Maybe she hadn't. I didn't know how high I was.

'Love you, Yas.' I lifted my hand and tangled our fingers, and I could feel Yas smile on my chest, in that same weird sensory way. Maybe it wasn't about the mystery of the senses, it was just about the mystery of Yas, of Yas and me. I was more with her, better. I sensed more. Yas made me expansive. Yas made me breathe myself into unknown and unfathomable skies.

'Sleep here,' Yas murmured, and her breathing evened. I kept twisting this idea, that my senses were just more open with her, in my smoky head until I fell asleep too.

'We're all in a really difficult position,' said Carolyn, my supervisor, waiting a beat too long before she added, 'these days.' She went on, 'I can understand wanting to take a stand. But it's a requirement of the job that we maintain a certain stance. Suppose one of your advisees was a veteran?'

'Some vets are anti-war,' I said. Carolyn looked at me. 'Anyway, I don't have any.'

'I have two,' said Carolyn. 'They could request a new advisor at any time, due to any kind of schedule change. But in many ways that's beside the point. We can't appear to be taking a political side in this office.'

'So what are you saying?' I was looking to the wall behind the left side of her face, my posture slouchy as an insubordinate teenager's.

'You can't attend a student-run and student-initiated protest,' Carolyn said. 'Not on campus. What you do on your own time — well, is your own time, and unless you're planning to commit some kind of vandalism or get arrested, what we don't know won't hurt us. But this — we know this. And we can't. It's not something we should know. Be able to know.'

'This is an issue I feel strongly about.'

'Do you think you're the only one in this office with strong feelings?' I was surprised to see Carolyn's eyes glistening. 'None of us enjoys this, Shannon. This isn't a good time for anyone.'

'George Bush seems to be doing fine.'

'Again, this is not something we can discuss in this space and at this time.'

Carolyn watched me, insistent on affirmation. Her hand took on a claw shape along the seam of her gray suit skirt. 'I understand,' I said. Technically it was the truth. She gave a crisp nod and informed me that for the rest of the semester Mariah, the receptionist, would be charged with managing all of our calendars; appointments were now to go through her. I wondered if Mariah, whose primary job seemed to be playing Snood, had been informed. When Carolyn left my office, I watched the back of Mariah's head and the disintegrating wall of cartoon faces on her screen through the half-open door.

'Turn it off,' Yas said that night.

'It's gross, isn't it?'

'I'm serious. Turn it the fuck off.'

I turned it off. 'Fuck' was another one of those words where Yas had a bit of a British lilt, and normally I would say, 'Sure, I'll turn it the bollocks off! I'll turn it the bloody hell off!' Instead, I looked at the black screen where George W. Bush, with his simian facial expressions and goofy diction, had been standing with a 'Mission Accomplished' banner rippling above him. I said, 'Did I ever tell you that during the 2000 elections, a guy I knew at school did a "Monkey versus Robot" movie series?'

'Yeah. Several times.' She blinked, mascara clumping on her lower lashes. '*Planet of the Apes* and all that shit.'

'Mystery Science Theater 3000.'

'I don't know what that is.'

'I didn't either before I saw them. It's funny, though.'

'Yeah? Good.'

'*Will* it be easier now?' I asked her. 'I mean, not like … but, you know, for Mostafa. Your mom's family. Without Saddam?'

'I don't know, Shan. Easier than what?' She sat down and leaned heavily against me; I hadn't been expecting her full weight and caught myself with my right hand. I could feel her spine, the angles of several vertebrae, through the red cotton of her pajama top. I reached for the bare skin I could find, rubbing the softness of her side in a tight, limited circle.

After a few minutes I said, 'Sorry.'

'Yeah? Why?'

My hand stopped moving, but I kept the top of my hand against her skin and felt her breathing. 'I guess I just wanted there to be something decent that comes out of all this. Even just, like, one tiny okay thing. A silver lining. You know?'

Yas shrugged. Her shoulder hit me just above my boob, and her hair brushed under my jaw. 'There might be. I don't know. It doesn't matter.'

After she kissed my forehead and went to bed, I turned the TV back on and watched gelled and lipsticked analysts dissect the contradictions in the President's speech: why he had a Mission Accomplished banner but hadn't said those words, what the end of major combat operations actually meant, whether their distant soldier cousins were coming home.

When I returned to the vigils, slipping in between Kayla and the pink-haired girl as if the spot were rightfully mine, the bass gave me a little smile as we sang 'Peace Like a River.' I had come to need the vigils almost the way I'd needed Yas at first, like a kidney. Their removal would be agonizing. I'd only do it to save myself or someone else. Even the litany of atrocities reassured me somehow, perhaps because someone else was reading it. I wasn't the only one scouring the media for data; in fact, I didn't have to look at all in order to know, to take on the burden of knowing as if I could lift it from Yas.

It wasn't until the second Friday, when I'd cancelled on Marissa Parker twice in two weeks, that Carolyn informed me Marissa had requested a switch to another advisor and she was wondering what I thought I could do to alleviate this situation. All I could think of to say was, 'I don't think we have a situation.'

Carolyn nodded briskly, her lips together. 'I think it's better if we don't — don't anymore,' she said. 'If this is bothering you so much … I think it's better if you take some time.'

'I'm sorry?'

'In two weeks, I think,' Carolyn said. 'We'll want to phase out the students who are still with you, and it gives you time to share your notes with the rest of the group.'

Yas was still at the table when I told her. 'You what?'

'I think I get severance.' I swallowed the salad knotting tightly in my throat. 'I'll be okay for a little while.'

'Because you were going to *vigils*? What the fuck, Shan?'

'They're — they're like protests.'

'Vigils, protests, who cares?'

Her anger shot into my limbs, and to fight it off, I said quickly, 'I did it for you.'

She stood up as if to go to our room, like she did so many nights, but instead she leaned over the back of the chair, wrapping hands and forearms through thin wooden bars. 'Did you, like, think you were going to stop the war? It wasn't for me. I knew you weren't going to stop the fucking war.'

'I had to try,' I said. I wasn't sure what I meant.

'Maybe sometimes I want a day off. Maybe I want to quit my job. Or take care of my father. Did you think about that?' I shook my head even though she wasn't really asking, or looking at me. Her eyes were fixed to our exposed brick wall, the block print that hung crookedly there. 'This same passive bullshit. Always.'

'Excuse me?' I said.

'It's like having a dog or something. You just roll over and want me to pat your goddamn belly.'

I stood too, pacing the kitchen wall. I felt like my footfalls were burning a trail along the floor. 'I'm sorry you have a girlfriend who cares about you.'

'Or like your mom. As long as you can prove what you're doing is the right thing—'

'Okay, so what if it was for me?' I heard myself shouting, trying to fight off the blow. 'Do I get to do something that matters to me? Or are you in charge of all of it?'

'Fuck off, Shan.'

I was blinking rapidly. Yas grabbed our plates from the table, stacked them on top of each other, and placed them in the sink, oddly noiseless. I was startled when she turned on the water. For the rest of the evening I kept listening for her voice, waiting for her to speak over the water running and the music playing in the background, but she was quiet.

A Diamond in this Rhinestone World

'Hey, Lizard,' says Jax, 'they changed the Jesus sign.'

We pause outside the Holy Immaculate Church, it's visage stark white in the desert heat. A giant plywood Jesus with beady black eyes stands next to a sign that looks like an old movie theater marquee. Since moving in with Jax to her trailer outside town, the sign has been changed three times. Now it says 'Jesus Saves,' which is pretty lazy to be honest.

If you squint, Jesus almost looks like he's winking. The paint on his beard has almost peeled all the way off.

'Jesus shaves,' I say.

'Jesus slaves,' says Jax.

We watch the old ladies in sun hats as they try to find their cars in the parking lot. Jax was raised Catholic so she's allowed some bitterness.

'I'm glad I was part of an outlier cult,' I say, 'and not some dumb mainstream one.'

'You mean your mother,' Jax corrects. 'Your mother was in a cult.' And she's right. I wasn't taught to pray to anything. I wasn't even raised to call anyone 'mother'.

'You never told me which cult though,' Jax adds, and she hits the gas and we speed away.

'I don't know which one,' I shout, though I do.

'Lizards lie,' I add as she drives fast, the wind stealing my voice. 'Lizards die,' I say as she goes faster.

As we hit a pothole, all my bones rattle.

'Oh shit,' says Jax.

On smooth ground she says, 'Oh yes. Lizards ride.'

I make lists of the things I'm not afraid of: rattling snakes or jumping spiders, damp crawl spaces or steep drops.

I'm not afraid of being swallowed by a sinkhole or quicksand.

I'm not afraid of drinking too much whiskey in the desert.

Five months ago, at a party, I met Jax while lying in a wheelbarrow with a bottle of Jack in my hand.

On the way to the party the Jesus sign said, 'God responds to knee-mail.'

I asked Jax if that sounded dirty. She asked me if anyone uses email anymore.

A girl at my new job at the co-op had invited me to the party, which was on an abandoned ranch her friends owned. All I knew about her was that her nose ring was always infected.

I don't mind going to parties and not knowing anyone, since my body has already detached itself from me. I float behind it like a balloon.

I'm not afraid of sharp objects or loud popping sounds.

I'm not afraid of strangers because I am one.

It wasn't until I met Jax while lying in a dusty wheelbarrow that I knew why I was here.

We wandered around far from the noise of the party, out into the desert. We pretended we were advertising a relaxing retreat that was secretly a scam.

'For a low rate of 2k a weekend, this will be your spiritual sanctuary,' I motioned at the darkened landscape.

'Roll in the dirt,' Jax said. 'It's good for your skin!'

'Stick cactus needles into your face to achieve clarity!'

'Dance with rattlesnakes! It's good for your aura!'

'If you get bit though,' I said, 'you have to suck out your own poison.'

Jax pointed to my whiskey. 'Give me some of that poison,' she said. When I handed the bottle to her, our hands touched and I felt like they've been touching my whole life.

That night, I could've eaten the stars.

I could've spit out light.

Two months later, my aunt Darlene kicked me off her ranch, which was a real ranch, and Jax asked me if I wanted to move in with her.

'She sounds like a nutcase,' Jax said when I told her how she threw all my bags on the lawn like I was a cheating husband.

'It runs in the family,' I said, though I hoped she wouldn't ask me to elaborate.

Me and Jax are both artists, or at least Jax is. Mostly she paints on found objects. She collects her loot from junkyards: scrap metal and porcelain tubs, wooden furniture that she dismantles and sands down. Outside in the yard, the sculptures stay, withstanding the heat and occasional rain.

Sometimes she paints portraits of her friends and family, usually in sad blues, or red and orange in ecstasy. Sitting near her while she works, I like to smell the paint, the colors of my only two emotions, when I have emotions.

Jax's biggest muse, though, is Dolly Parton. She paints her with a halo like a saint. Around Dolly's famous wig, Jax glues on welded stars, metal butterflies, and rhinestones. The rhinestones usually fall off though, leaving perfect white circles.

Now she's writing a Dolly quote along the inside of a tub: 'It's hard to be a diamond in a rhinestone world.'

Jax wants to paint me and every so often she mentions it.

'Paint my face on Dolly's body,' I say, though I know it's blasphemy.

'You want this hair?' asks Jax.

'No, the big breasts,' I say, because I know she won't say it.

'Obviously,' she chuckles, knowing I won't be hurt.

I used to be a sculptor. My work always resembled the ways my body ached: balloons like stomachs pumped with pink ooze, silk stockings like intestines stuffed with newspapers, candle wax formed into globs like melted skin.

But now I'm stuck on repeat, painting El Camino Hotel, over and over again.

Its pale exterior is bleached into my brain because it's the last place I saw my mother. I remember her standing in the parking lot wearing a green hippie skirt that flowed around her ankles. Though she parked the car on the side of the road instead of in the parking lot, she told me to sit on the curb right in front of the El Camino and wait.

'I'll be right back, Lizbeth,' she said, but she never returned.

In front of the El Camino by the road there's a giant cowboy holding the sign. He's plywood like the Jesus in front of Holy Immaculate Church. The cowboy wears shotgun chaps, a large brown cowboy hat, and a blue shirt that almost blends into the sky. He doesn't resemble anyone I know. The Jesus, though, looks like the boys I would meet in smoky basements, undeserving boys with ratty hair, who I let inside me again and again, wanting something from them I couldn't name.

I paint the cowboy too, of course, but he always looks too flat, though he's supposed to be flat.

'Artistic liberty,' I say sometimes whenever I get something wrong. But 'artist' was always a word I could only chew on like the sweet meat of an orange, unable to get the good part off the rind, the juice of it running down my chin, sticky and wet.

'All I am is *sticky*,' I say as I paint the El Camino Hotel windows for the zillionth time. They are the only thing that changes. Now they are tinted blue, the light color in the shine of an oyster shell.

'That's even better than the last one,' says Jax.

With blue paint, I draw a lopsided star on her temple just below her hair line. Its shimmer is noticeable in the desert sun.

'Shiny like a rhinestone,' I say, waiting for her to lick her thumb and rub it off, but she doesn't.

Instead she tilts her head and shows it off, squinting.

'You'd be surprised how much it costs,' she says, 'to look this cheap,' quoting Saint Iron Butterfly herself.

Jax knows the story of the El Camino Hotel though she doesn't know about my life before: my childhood on the Chesapeake Bay, our thirty-plus hour journey west, everything that happened after.

When I was left at El Camino, it took me too long to realize my mother wasn't going to return. This happened sixteen years ago when I was seven years old.

Sitting alone for maybe hours on a curb, I told myself I wasn't a child. Tears didn't well in my eyes. Taking mulch from under the bushes in the front, I threw one chip after the other into the parking lot. Birds gathered, confused, pecking at the pieces before flying away.

The cowboy loomed in the parking lot, his shadow stretching, slowly moving across the cars until strangers approached me and asked, 'Are you okay? Where is your mother?'

I wasn't a child. I didn't cry.

'Well,' says Jax. 'Then what happened?'

I don't tell her how everything after is just a blur, one relative after another, one rejection to the next. I see that parade of years as a haze, behind fogged glass. I can only allow myself this.

I shrug. 'I went to the desert,' I say. 'You found me in a wheelbarrow.'

'You fell down with the rain,' she says.

'A rain of whiskey,' I say.

I try to make lists of the things I am afraid of but it always just boils down to one.

On bad days, I think of the worst I've read: cult members in Nikes eating poisoned applesauce, cult members sex trafficked and burned alive, cults members forced to scrub ships with toothbrushes. One false move and you're forced to walk the plank.

I haven't said my mother's name in years. I kept calling her 'my mother' to everyone who's never met her until, even to me, she just became that word, no smell attached, no sight, no memory of skin.

I wish my aunt never told me the name of the cult that took her.

Sometimes you avoid the details because you don't want to know what really happened. Ignorance is bliss.

'Ignorance is taking a piss,' Jax has said. 'Being apolitical is a political act.'

Jax was kicked out of her house at sixteen for being in love with a woman, her violin teacher who was in her thirties.

'My parent's problem wasn't the age difference,' Jax said, 'so they totally missed the real issue.'

Recently, the Jesus sign said, 'God is in the details.'

'I thought it was the devil,' said Jax.

'I'm going to take a magnifying glass,' I said. 'I'm going to see which one.'

Sometimes we all need someone to blame.

That day my aunt kicked me off her ranch, my body burned all over.

The night before there was a full moon and I was rabid.

I could feel spikes growing out of my skin, my head hot, everything going white.

I don't remember what triggered it but I was shouting, crying, breaking plates on the floor, beating my head against the wall.

Once it was over, Aunt Darlene looked afraid at first, then her fear turned to anger.

'What a spoiled brat you are,' she said. She pulled up my long sleeves and saw all the scars I made on my arms in a moment of fury. 'How selfish,' she said, her eyes dead to me.

I didn't get to say goodbye to the cows on her ranch that I used to kiss, gazing into their big eyes with long lashes. I didn't get to say goodbye to my uncle Jim who was out feeding the animals at the time, and he was always kind to me.

'You did this to yourself,' my aunt had said, and it hurt the most because I knew it was true.

'It's like an itch,' I say to myself in the trailer's small bathroom mirror. 'It's like wanting a cigarette.' I practice this explanation for Jax if she ever asks about the scars. I imagine her nodding as she lights a Camel but I never get to say it because she never asks.

I've been having trouble eating because my stomach always hurts, the pain riding up into my chest, burning. Sometimes, my body spikes sharp and I wish I could shed my skin like a reptile, crawl out and leave it behind in the desert. Then I'd walk for miles, naked in the hazy heat. I'd pull off my sinewy muscles, pick all the meat off my bones. Next, I'd dismantle my skeleton piece by piece, starting with the smallest bits in my middle ear, digging deep, but even then I could still hear myself think.

My thoughts would go to the Jesus sign saying, 'You should hunger and thirst everyday,' but I forget the rest.

One day, Jax gives in and allows me to be Dolly. She brings out the same colors I've been using for the windows of the El Camino hotel — blues and greens and oranges.

'You can paint on my skin instead,' I tell Jax as consolation. One time, a boy I was seeing told me that I should cover my scars with tattoos of beautiful roses.

'How about the desert thorn-apple instead?' I asked him, explaining its fragile trumpet blossom, deadly as a nightshade.

'Wow,' he scoffed. 'You're edgy.'

Like a blade, I would've joked if I wasn't desperately afraid he would leave me. But, even now, I don't joke about blades.

From the internet, I've learned different ways to calm myself down. Leave the room, picture someone you admire, take deep breaths, squeeze an ice cube, concentrate on the shock of it, the water trickling through your clenched fist.

Sometimes it works. Sometimes it doesn't.

'I changed my mind,' I say to Jax, 'I don't want to be painted today.'

She nods in understanding.

Every night Jax and I watch our favorite movies: *Harold and Maude, Desperately Seeking Susan, Thelma and Louise*.

Jax has a projector and white shower curtain she pulls down behind the couch. The back of the couch holds the screen in place, making it taut. Since the couch is in use, we sit on stools, our backs toward the narrow kitchen. Sometimes there's a wrinkle on the screen, some of the scenery distorted. Other times one of us, usually me, kneels on the couch and acts out the scene, the actor's face ghostly and crooked on my own.

'I don't remember ever feeling this awake,' I quote the line dramatically, way off cue as strands of Louise's hair ripple over my face.

Later, I try to sleep on the couch, but my bones ache from lack of touch. In a whiskey daze, I go to the end of the trailer where Jax's bedroom is. I creak open the door and slip in. Crawling into her bed, I feel her warmth as I move my hand slowly down her arm then back up again. Brushing the tendrils of her hair aside, I kiss her neck.

She wakes up and nudges me away.

'Stop it, Liz,' she mutters, and I roll onto my back, my skin on fire.
'Later?' I ask, but she pretends to be asleep.

The next morning, Jax doesn't mention the previous night and I'm relieved, hoping she was too sleepy to remember. I had left her bed before dawn broke, crawled back onto the couch, hungover in shame. As my body burned, I rolled over and buried my head into the back of the couch to muffle my sobbing.

Now Jax is buying a tattoo kit online. She already has a stick and poke kit which she has only used on herself. Small stars and circles and moons are etched around her ankles, on the soft skin of her thighs.

But now she needs the real deal since she wants to practice before she apprentices her friend Darrel who works at a tattoo parlor in town.

Even so, Jax seems to hesitate before clicking the purchase button.

'You'd be good at that,' I say.

Jax sits up straight, her arm resting on the top of the couch.

'Lizbeth, being serious for once!'

'Aren't I Lizard?' I ask, endeared by the nickname only she uses, but also glad again to hear my birth name. 'Yes, I am serious,' I say, wondering how many incarnations of Dolly will be on customers' biceps. 'You're talented,' I add and it's true, she's the most talented person I know.

'I have more talent than guts,' says Jax, turning the Dolly quote around.

I decide to quit drinking and, like a newly sober asshole, I declare, 'I'm quitting drinking!'

'Since when?' asks Jax.

'Since this second.'

'Until when?'

I shrug.

'Well, darlin', look out,' I say, 'cause my hair is comin' down,' quoting Thelma this time.

Both sober, Jax teaches me blackjack. With fast hands, she pulls the cards out like a pro. Jax got this trailer from cheating at casino games, mostly slot machines, but she won't give away any of the details. So we both have hands we hold close to our chests.

Now, she plays the dealer, of course.

I'm learning that I shouldn't be gambling. I throw my chips in without thinking. I'm too quick in placing my bet.

'You're two thousand in the hole, Liz,' says Jax.

'I guess the house will have to break my knees. Unless you teach me some tricks.'

'My cheatin' days are over,' says Jax like a cowboy, leaning back, putting her boots on the table as she lights a cigarette.

I show her magic tricks to redeem myself. I read her mind again and again but that's all it is, a trick.

'Sorry, I can't teach you,' I say. 'Magician's code.'

'It's all right,' she says. 'You got all the magic I need, baby.'

And that's when I kiss her. To my surprise, we don't stop kissing.

'Are you sure?' Jax keeps repeating and I say 'yes' and it's true, I've never been so sure of anything in my life.

After we stumble to her room and onto her bed in the dark, I move down the length of her body. We linger here, in soft comfort of what it might've felt like to be a child, the two of us, still young, under the covers, reborn.

It'll be my birthday in a week. I'll be twenty four, as old as my mother was when she had me.

'I'm going to make you a cake,' says Jax, though she doesn't know how to make a cake.

'No, you won't,' I say.

I imagine my mother pregnant with me, unable to eat. She told me that even the smell of her favorite foods made her nauseous. I see her back then, a shell of a mother, hollow with the fetus of me rattling inside.

I was born on her birthday. On her way to get dinner with her coworkers, her water broke in her office building elevator.

'You ruined my birthday dinner,' she joked, but it turned into a tape on repeat after she left. Ruined ruined ruined.

I wonder if she's eating well. I wonder if she ever touches the scar on her stomach where I came out. I wonder if it's faded, barely noticeable, as if I never had an origin at all.

The last Jesus sign I saw said, 'The more you feed your faith, the more you'll starve your fear,' and it made my stomach ache.

'I want a Pepto Bismol punch,' I say to Jax. 'Pour some Mylanta on me and lick it off.'

She laughs quietly in her Jax way.

'All right,' she says. 'I'll crush some Tums. Tums sprinkles, how about that?'

She asks me what I want for my birthday and the words come out before I can stop them.

'To go to the El Camino,' I say as though my intestine has grown teeth, trying to gnaw itself out from me. I touch my skin as if I could feel its sharpness, but I can't.

'Are you sure?' says Jax with a different concern then when she asked if it was okay when I touched her.

I nod slowly.

We decide to drive out early in the morning. We pack a suitcase on my insistence.

'If you want to stay,' I say, 'for the night.'

Jax chuckles. 'If I do,' she says, almostly mockingly, not wanting to take the responsibility as her own.

We drive in Jax's convertible with the top down. I try to concentrate on the road stretching on before us, but my hair is whipping too much in my face.

I wonder if I actually remember the El Camino correctly. It's memory flickers like a projected movie, but other places and people obstruct the view as it ripples over them.

I look at Jax, her hair tied back tight, and I wonder if I'll regret what's growing between us. I wish I had an ice cube to hold, a sharpness piercing straight to the bone.

When we get to the El Camino, I'm surprised at how accurate my paintings are. There stands the same pale stucco exterior, the cowboy with his large brown hat, grinning, cartoonishly flat.

The windows aren't blinking colors though because it's still too early. The sun isn't even setting yet and I wonder how long we can stay.

But did I ever see the windows light up the first pace? I can't imagine what color they'd be, which version is right. I want to close my eyes and see them flashing but I know I won't.

There are no people in the parking lot except for a woman who has her back to us. Standing completely still, she stares up at the cowboy sign.

Immediately, I recognize her—the slight sideways lean, the ugly paisley hippie dress shimmering right under her knee.

My heart latches in my chest. My mother. Her dirty blonde hair flows down her back, it almost looks wet, so much so I want to put it in my mouth and suck it dry.

When my mother turns around for a moment to go into her backpack, I immediately realize it's not her at all, only a stranger.

There's a sudden acute pain of loss, not because she isn't my mother, but because I know with a bittersweetness that I'll never paint The El Camino again.

'I was born here,' I say out of nowhere. 'This is my mother.' I wave my hand around and cry out, 'The El Camino is my mother!'

The lady doesn't turn to us. She doesn't even flinch.

'And that cowboy is daddy,' Jax says and I laugh.

'The only true daddy,' I say and the woman clicks the camera. I realize she's an idiot because she used the flash even in this bright sun.

On the way home, a slight cold breeze hits as the sun sets but Jax leaves the top down.

I tell her the story of the time I caught a water moccasin. As a child, six or seven, I stood among the cattails in the creek off the Chesapeake, trying to catch minnows with a butterfly net. A black snake came right up to me, slithering in the brackish water, seeming to float on the surface like Jesus himself. Swiftly I scooped him up with the net. When I threw him onto the grass, he began to dart toward my pointed wooden house. So I kept scooping him up in my net and he kept jumping out, determined, wriggling toward my home. Finally, I threw him into the blue plastic trash bin that my mother kept on the side of the house and slammed the lid down. I yelled for my mother and ran inside. She had her back to me, washing dishes, and I yanked on her sleeve, pleading with her to come out and see what I caught.

A type of electricity rushed through me. Did I want her to be proud of me or afraid? As I opened the lid, the snake leaped out and she gasped, hand on her chest.

'Wait,' she said, as the snake made his way back to the creek. 'Is that the trash bin I use for the dog poop? Put it back.'

Jax laughs.

'Is that why you like snakes?' she asks, and I admire her bravery.

'I am the snake,' I say, and even through the wind I know she hears me.

The next day, Jax's tattoo gun still hasn't arrived in the mail.

'Stick and poke my skin, baby,' I say, and she doesn't even hesitate. Taking the unlit cigarette from her lips, she goes to get her kit.

She dips the needle in the inkwell and pierces my arm with it. She does this again and again: a small cross, a tiny butterfly, a lopsided star.

With each puncture, I wish my skin would turn inside out. I wish the ink was her spit, the needle a tooth filled with poison.

But instead I watch her concentrate, her brow furrowed, a deep wrinkle forming between her eyebrows which will only get deeper as she grows old.

As she starts to make a snake on my arm, inch by inch, and I want to say *I love you I love you* when she doesn't touch a scar, not a single one.

STEPHANIE EARLY GREEN

The Hall of Human Origins

The Natural History Museum reopened in April, after being closed for over a year. The cherry trees had bloomed the week before and had already begun littering the sidewalks with their blossoms. That was one thing that had stayed the same, even as everything else had changed: every year, the cherry blossoms burst forth, lasted a week, then dropped dead. The year before, we'd missed the cherry blossoms because we'd been in lockdown, in a neighborhood that hadn't received any cherry trees from Japan a hundred years earlier. Our street was crowded with rowhouses, brick on brick on brick, and the tree-lawns were planted with spindly saplings that were so weak they had to be scaffolded.

This year, though, with the virus gone and our arms still sore from the miracle shot, Greg and I were going to see the cherry blossoms. We were going to sit on a grassy beach along the Potomac and gaze over the chocolate milk water at the lacy pink cherry blossoms and say, 'Aren't we lucky, to live in a place like this?' We'd almost forgotten what lucky felt like.

* * *

We'd been surprised at how easily we'd adjusted to our new circumstances. In those first, awful weeks of the virus, after people had started perishing in droves and the country had installed a new emergency Congress, a new President, and new joint Chiefs of Staff, the world had felt raw and oozing, like a wound with its stitches ripped out. But the lesion scabbed over quickly. We got used to the feeling of being bored and terrified at the same time. We figured, well, this is how things are now. At least we have each other. At least we're not trapped in a house with people we hate. At least we have food on the table. At least we're alive and healthy, with bodies that can move and breathe and cry and sleep. At least.

Greg and I said over and over how grateful we were to be alive, but some days, I didn't feel grateful. I felt like a husk, a body shuffling through the motions of a tiny life: making the coffee, sitting in the chair, turning on the computer. No going outside, except for food or medicine. No socializing. No fresh air. No exceptions. We would have stayed locked in, missing the blooming of the cherry trees every single year for the rest of our lives, if it weren't for the vaccine. The vaccine was a miracle: 100% effective. Doctors had never seen anything like it. A scientific marvel. A triumph!

We all rushed to get the shot. There were long lines. People brought drums and guitars. People handed out ice cream cones and bottles of water. People cried and laughed and hugged. To see other humans was a thrill and a balm. How comforting, to know that we weren't alone anymore.

As we stood in line for our shots, I put my arm around Greg's waist.

'Let's have a baby,' I said, loud enough that the gray-haired woman ahead of us in line turned and smirked.

Greg rubbed his chin with his palm and smiled. 'Okay,' he said, 'but can we wait until we get home?'

The gray-haired woman laughed, and we laughed, too.

*   *   *

A week after we got the shot, after its effects had fully sunk in, Greg and I packed a picnic. We would go to the Natural History Museum, which had reopened only the day before, and then wander down to the river to eat and drink and admire the cherry trees. We loaded a backpack with a bottle of sparkling wine, rounds of cheese, sleeves of crackers. Grocery shopping – touching an orange, seeing another person's face as they bent to examine a jar of pasta sauce, breathing in the scent of rotisserie chicken – was a novelty, and I'd filled my cart with frivolities: date crackers, star fruit, shrimp cocktail, cassava pretzels. Life, after all, was short. Why not taste everything, touch everything? We had to live while we could.

At the entrance to the museum, Greg went through the metal detector while I stopped at the security desk with the backpack. I was always the one who carried the bag, especially when we had something to hide, no matter how small: a pair of knitting needles, an electronic device, a bottle of Gatorade. I was the one to talk to security guards and cops and nosy neighbors. A White woman could giggle away her rule-breaking, say, *Oops, I forgot! Silly me.* If Greg tried that – well, forget it. Whenever Greg held the bag, even if the bag contained nothing at all, we got stopped. Airports, train stations, baseball stadiums, museums. *Sir, please step aside.* There was no point in trying to argue. They always had an excuse. Flickering taillight. Random screening. Suspicious odor.

So, I held the bag. I felt noble, shouldering this small burden. Greg never made me feel bad about the relative ease of my own life, the fact that holding the bag was the least I could have done. He let me think I was helping. He was a good husband, honestly. What happened later to me – to us – was simply too much for any human to bear.

At the museum, a security guard with pink-rimmed glasses on a chain around her neck peered inside the backpack, nosed around with a flashlight. I waited for her to confiscate the bubbly, the crackers, the cheeses. I began thinking of excuses, ways to wriggle out of consequences. But the security guard straightened, waved me past the metal detector, told me to have a good day. Greg was waiting at the wrinkled feet of the taxidermy elephant in the rotunda.

'Did they take anything?' he asked.

I shook my head.

'Of course not,' he said, but he smiled.

I wanted to go straight to the Hall of Gems and Minerals, where the Hope Diamond sat on its velvety dais. I liked to imagine holding the diamond's blue coolness in my fist, closing my fingers around its facets, popping it into my mouth like an egg. I liked to murmur the names of precious stones under my breath: chalcedony, agate, elbaite, afghanite, beryl. (I told Greg, once, that I wanted to name our first child Beryl. Boy or girl. Greg, to his credit, did not laugh. He said, 'Let's let that one simmer.')

But Greg insisted we do the museum 'in order.' Start at the bottom, go around, go up. That was Greg. Punctilious. Correct. His kind of orderliness would have driven some people crazy, but not me. We were a good match. We started on the ground floor, in the Hall of Human Origins. We wandered past the reconstructed heads of long-dead ancestors. Homo habilis. Paranthropus boisei. Homo rudolfensis. Homo erectus.

'Looks like your cousin Charlie,' said Greg, gesturing to homo neanderthalensis. He wasn't wrong. The heavy brow, the downturned mouth, the man bun: a strong resemblance. We paused in front of a Neanderthal skeleton laid out bone by bone, like a piece of Ikea furniture waiting to be assembled.

'Look how long the skull is,' I said. 'Weird to think we interbred with them.'

'Speak for yourself. My people did no such thing.'

'Yes, yes, I know. No Neanderthals in South Africa.'

'But even if there had been,' said Greg, grimacing. 'I mean, no offense.'

Almost a decade before this, Greg had taken me to South Africa to meet his parents, Joseph and Charity, for the first time. Joseph had arranged a day trip to the Cradle of Humankind, an hour's drive from their

81

home. The sky was white and cloudless, and the scent of baking grass rose up from the earth. Beyond the grass-domed visitors' center were limestone caves where, Joseph explained, paleontologists in the 1940s had discovered a 2.3-million-year-old Australopithecus africanus skull.

'Two point three *million* years,' said Joseph, jabbing a finger in the air to emphasize each word. 'This is where humanity began. Right here in Africa. People forget that, maybe, in the United States. Or perhaps they never knew, to begin with. But here, we remember.'

We bought tickets to the caves, eager to see the skull of our tiny ancestor who walked upright over these grasslands, ran for cover from swooping birds of prey, climbed stubby trees to evade giant cats. But the skull was not there: it was kept behind glass at a museum in Pretoria. Disappointed, we wandered through the dark, quiet caves, and then out through the visitors' center, where we examined a reconstruction of Australopithecus africanus, its flat face furry and guileless.

'What killed them off?' I asked.

'Climate change, most likely,' said Joseph. He looked at me, eyebrows raised. 'And other people, of course.'

'Well,' said Greg, 'that's natural selection, Dad. Are we meant to feel sorry for all of the prehistoric species that couldn't hack it?'

Joseph looked at his son over the tops of his spectacles. 'One day,' he said, '*we* will be one of those species who 'couldn't hack it.' And no, I won't feel a bit sorry for us.'

When the virus began to spread, last year, I remembered my father-in-law's words and wondered if this was what we'd had coming all along. Maybe our species just wasn't made to survive. But then, somehow, we did.

In the Natural History Museum, Greg and I stood in front of the Neanderthal skull, brown and distended, alien-looking. I looked away.

'C'mon, let's go to the Ocean Hall,' I said. 'I want to see that whale skeleton with legs.'

In truth, I wanted space from my ancestors. The beady eyes and judgy expression of homo nadeli made me uneasy. Homo floresiensis was scowling like she knew my darkest secrets. I'd never cared much about human origins, anyway. Why dwell on the past when the present was slipping away?

* * *

I started to feel sick a week after our visit to the museum.

'This is the thing about being out in public again,' said Greg, when I complained of a headache. 'Germs.'

Our immune systems, after all, had been on pause for a year, sheltering in place. But now germs were back, floating freely, attaching themselves to the insides of our noses, the corners of our eyes, the tips of our tongues. They were giving us runny noses and coughs and sneezes. Refreshing, really, to have a little cold and not worry about dropping dead, for once.

Or maybe, I let myself think, *I'm pregnant*. I'd stopped taking my birth control two weeks earlier. Maybe we'd gotten lucky on the first try. I closed my eyes and saw a baby, small as a grain of rice, teeny tiny fingers and toes curled, its pink heart fluttering in a translucent chest. Hope began radiating from my belly, pumping through my veins like a virus. I made no effort to combat the spread. I let the hope consume me.

But it soon became clear that I was not pregnant, only sick. My head and muscles ached. I trembled with fever. My mouth was dry, my eyes burned. I didn't tell Greg about the rice-grain baby, my silly, raging hope. Instead, I told him I had a cold, and tried to feel grateful. *At least I'm alive*, I thought. By the second day, though, I'd begun to worry that the vaccine hadn't worked, that I was the one exception to the rule, that the virus had outsmarted the miracle drug. Greg talked me off the ledge. The virus was gastrointestinal, he reminded me, and started, in 85% of cases, with stomach cramping. No above-the-neck symptoms.

'It's probably allergies,' Greg said.

He opened an app on his phone that showed the pollen count. DC was bright red, a bloodbath of tree detritus. I'd never had allergies before, but the virus had scrambled my understanding of health and illness. Maybe I was an allergy sufferer now. Better, as we'd taken to saying, than the alternative.

On the third day, I couldn't get out of bed. My headache was blinding, as if the bones in my skull were cracking open. I moaned in bed, a cool washcloth pressed to my pulsing forehead. Greg came into the room, which I'd made dark as a womb. I didn't open my eyes, but could feel his weight on the edge of the bed.

'Can I get you anything?' he asked. 'Tylenol? Or I could make you some ginger tea. You want tea?'

I couldn't answer.

'Try to get some sleep,' Greg said, patting my leg through the covers, and left the room.

That night was the worst. Every heartbeat throbbed in my head and neck. I didn't turn on the light because I knew that I needed to be in the dark, to get through whatever was happening. I felt like a laboring mammal, searching out a safe nest. I pulled the covers over my face and breathed through clenched teeth. By the morning, the pain in my head had eased to a dull throbbing, like a hangover. But the rest of my body ached, especially my joints, which felt swollen and stiff. The room was dark and musty. I smelled my own sweat on my pillow.

Greg came in, holding a white paper bag and a cup of tea. 'Went to CVS,' he said, 'and cleared out the cold and allergy shelf. And I made you some ginger tea. You can't beat ginger tea for a cold. At least, that's what Mum always says, so – I'm gonna turn on the light, okay?'

Before I could respond, he'd flipped on the overhead light. My eyes smarted and I covered them with my hands. My forehead felt bulbous. My hands, too, felt alien on my own face, like two baseball mitts. I cracked open my eyes and saw my husband staring at me. I had seen Greg afraid – really afraid – a handful of times. The time Joseph had called in the middle of the night to say that Charity had been rushed to the hospital for an emergency appendectomy. The time we were pulled over by the Virginia State Police while driving on a pitch-dark road outside Shenandoah National Park. The cop had rapped on the driver's side window with his flashlight, making us jump. He'd ordered Greg out of the car, made him stand in the glare of the police car's headlights, his palms sweating against the side of our car, while the cop frisked him for weapons he didn't have. When Greg got back in the car, he was trembling. We drove back to the cabin we'd rented in silence. It had been our anniversary weekend. A nice little getaway.

The last time I'd seen real fear on Greg's face was the day the President died. Until now.

Greg dropped the bag and the mug of ginger tea. The hot liquid steamed up from the hardwood floor.

'What?' I asked, feeling my lumpen face with my hands. 'What's wrong?' My words were garbled, my tongue thick in my mouth.

'You –' Greg shook his head. 'You – changed.'

* * *

Millions of people all over the world had been affected, the news said. Europe had been hit particularly hard. I could understand everything – the news, Greg, the doctors – but no one could understand me. My mouth no longer fit together properly. My jaw had shifted forward, my chin had receded back. My teeth had grown wide and square. When I touched them, they felt like wax teeth, a Halloween gag. I refused to look in the mirror. I could tell by the way Greg looked at me, with the whites of his eyes, that I didn't want to see.

Theories began to circulate about why a large chunk of the population had changed. The evidence was anecdotal, scattered, but the pattern was obvious: for the most part, White people had changed. Others had not. The growing consensus among scientists was that the vaccine had triggered something – a 'gene cascade,' they called it – in certain people. Not every White person had changed, only some of us. The unlucky. The cursed. The genetically inferior.

The doctors asked how I felt. I tried to explain, but they couldn't understand. My craggy hands could still hold a pen, so I wrote notes. My handwriting was horrible.

'How do you feel?' one of the doctors asked.

'Awful,' I scrawled.

'Pain?'

I shook my head.

The doctor, whose name badge said Dr. Tina Yeh, MD, nodded. 'This must be scary,' she said. Her hand hovered over mine, but did not make contact. She pulled back, tucked her hand into the pocket of her lab coat.

A tear slipped down my wide, puffy cheek. It was good to know I could still cry, at least.

* * *

For the first weeks, Greg slept in the same bed with me.

'I still love you,' he said, holding my knobby Neanderthal hands in his slender, homo sapien ones. 'Okay? This doesn't change that.'

I nodded, wanting to believe him. But he seemed uneasy around me, as if he were afraid I'd spring on him, beat him over the head with a club. *It's me*, I wanted to say. *It's still me.* But I had changed. The physical shifts were immediate and obvious: the brow-ridge, the prognathic jaw and recessed chin, the wide bones and stocky build. But the other changes were as subtle as ice melting. I began to crave fatty cuts of meat, bloody. Filets of salmon, tiny bones glistening. Handfuls of dandelions ripped from the tiny patch of grass in our backyard. I chewed on tree bark in between meals. The roughness felt good on my new teeth.

After a while, Greg started sleeping in the guest room.

* * *

In the first few months after The Change, there had been some hope that the gene cascade was temporary, or could be reversed. But as the months went on, hope for a cure dwindled. We, the New Neanderthals, had reverted to an earlier stage of human development, one buried in the depths of our genes. We could go backwards, but not forwards. When it became clear that I would never again be normal – never regain the ability to speak intelligibly, or wear shoes, or drive a car – I was bereft. Some days, I cried for hours. These crying jags were ferocious, tidal. They pulled me out to sea. I made noises like an animal, snuffling and grunting. Greg sat next to me on the bed and rubbed my back, trying not to look repulsed as he touched my leathery skin. Through my tears, I scrawled self-pitying notes: 'This is so unfair' and 'Why me?' Greg nodded, and handed me Kleenex, and said things like, 'This must be so hard for you,' and 'I can't imagine.' He sat with me for as long as he could bear. Hours and hours. Then, inevitably, he'd need to go to work, or the grocery store, or the gym. I'd cry the whole time he was gone.

But one day, Greg read online that because Neanderthal brains had smaller temporal lobes, we lacked the ability to regulate emotions: that we were, essentially, toddlers. Experts advised that partners and caregivers of New Neanderthals treat us with patience but firmness. Boundaries, the experts stressed, were important. Greg began to ignore my crying. He stopped handing me Kleenex, rubbing my back. Soon, he stopped touching me altogether.

* * *

After a while, my tears ebbed on their own. I got out of bed with the urge to walk. Barefoot, I roamed through every quadrant of the Capital. I trod over broken glass, gravel, litter. Nothing penetrated. On my first few walks, I only saw unchanged people: sitting on their porches, trimming their hedges, pushing babies in strollers. They either averted their eyes or stared openly. No one said hello, or commented on the lovely weather, the naked cherry trees, the cloudless skies. But then, I started to see other people like me. We were all out wandering, searching for something we couldn't name. We nodded to each other. At first, we tried not to look at the other people, the unchanged. Looking at them was too painful. After a while, though, we stopped noticing them.

One day, I was lumbering down 23rd Street past the entrance to GW University Hospital, when the glass doors to the lobby slid open. Through the doors, an orderly pushed a wheelchair containing a woman cradling a newborn baby. The mother had a pale, tired face. She gazed down at the baby in her arms, wrapped like a burrito in a white and pink striped blanket. I stopped walking to let them pass. When the mother saw me, she flinched and pulled the baby closer to her chest. I wanted to tell her, *Your baby is beautiful*. But I'd learned that trying to speak to the unchanged was hopeless. They never understood. I felt tears rising in my throat. I wanted to turn back to the mother with the baby. *I could have been you*, I wanted to shout at her. *I should have been you*.

I turned for home, my heart pounding in my barrel chest, desperate to see Greg. I found him in the kitchen, making a turkey sandwich. The turkey stank of chemicals; the mustard burned my eyes. Greg blinked at me, trying to arrange his face into a neutral expression. It had been months since I'd changed, but still, every time I entered a room, my husband looked startled. He laid a Kosher pickle on the side of his plate, closed the jar. I felt a surge of tenderness for him, then, with his neat arrangement of plate, sandwich, and pickle, but my clumsy face could no longer express my feelings. I felt tears coming on and tried to stanch them. Greg hated when I cried, now.

'Can I help with something?' he asked, sounding like an employee at a big box store, offering to assist a customer find a TV.

I grabbed a pen and pad – we'd begun keeping them around the house – and wrote a note. Greg squinted at my wretched handwriting before his neutral expression dissolved into confusion, then twisted into anger.

'Is this a joke?' he said, tossing the paper to the floor. 'You want to have a *baby*?'

He spat the last word.

I scribbled another note. *You wanted one before.*

'That was before. I mean – how could you even think about doing this to another person? A child?' He closed his eyes, like it hurt to look at me. 'Look, I know this is not your fault. But please – don't ask me to put someone else through this, too. Okay?'

He walked out of the kitchen so fast that the papers on the floor riffled in his wake. He left his lunch behind. I gathered the papers, crumpled them, and threw them into the trash. I dumped Greg's sandwich and pickle on top, burying the evidence. Then I yanked open the fridge and found a package of ground beef. I broke the seal of the plastic with my teeth. Tears streamed down my face as I ate.

* * *

Greg began avoiding me. When I entered a room, he left. If he caught sight of me, he cut his eyes away. I wanted to tell him that I loved him, that I knew he wanted a child, and that a baby was maybe the only thing I could still give him. But my hand cramped after holding a pencil for more than a few seconds. My notes became shorter and shorter, my handwriting worse and worse. Soon, I stopped writing notes. I stopped trying to explain myself.

Being in the house together was painful for both of us. I walked longer and longer distances, staying away. I crossed the Potomac into Virginia, then crossed the river again into Maryland. I passed rowhouses, harbors, restaurants, boat slips, casinos, monuments. Whenever I passed another person like me, I felt their sadness pulsing through the air like a current. I knew they could feel mine, too. After a while, instead of only nodding, we began brushing hands, touching foreheads. We looked into each other's faces and tried to see what we must have looked like, before. Then, after a while, we looked into each other's faces and saw only who we were now.

A small group of us began gathering under a bridge near the river. We set up a camp with tents and blankets. We figured out how to start fires, roast meats. We used sidewalk chalk to draw pictures on the cement walls of the bridge. We sang, as best we could. We beat a drum. We laughed. How good it was, to be with other people again.

There was sorrow, too, in what we could not say. We couldn't tell each other about our families, the people we'd left behind. I couldn't tell them about Greg: his straight posture, the dimple in his left cheek, the scar on his right ankle where, as a child, he'd scraped his skin to the bone against the stucco side of a pool. I couldn't tell them that we'd met in grad school, that we were both only children, that we used to worry about who would take care of our parents when they got old. My parents were in Minnesota and his were in Johannesburg and how would we ever bridge that gap? I couldn't tell them that I suspected my parents had changed, too – I hadn't heard a word from my mother since the gene cascade, and normally, she called every week – but now I was not capable of caring for anyone else, only myself.

But there was relief in not talking. There was relief in lying next to the warmth of other bodies, feeling others' hands and feet and faces. There was relief in knowing that, if nothing else, we would not be alone anymore.

* * *

The cherry trees bloomed gloriously the spring after The Change. From our camp, we had a clear view of the trees along the Potomac, white and pink and fluffy, shedding blossoms like confetti. Every morning, I woke to the rumble of traffic on the bridge overhead and the mewls of newborn babies. Spring was the time when babies were born, among our people. I was happy for the new mothers, but couldn't look for too long at the babies: their flat, scrunched faces, their tiny, balled hands. Instead, I gazed at the cherry trees and thought about Greg. I wondered if he would go and see the cherry blossoms. I wondered if, like last year, he'd pack a picnic, go to the Natural History Museum. I wondered if he'd have trouble at the security check-in. I wondered if, once he was through the metal detector, he'd start at the beginning, at the Hall of Human Origins, or if, for once in his life, he'd allow himself to do things out of order.

* * *

After The Change, I stopped dreaming. When I closed my eyes, I was plunged into blankness until I awoke. But a year and a half after I'd left Greg, I dreamt he was beside me. I could see his face, relaxed in sleep, his hands open like a child's. I rolled over, reaching for him, but when I opened my eyes, I was on the blue sleeping tarp under the bridge, surrounded by other hairy bodies. A baby squalled, a mother shushed. Greg was not there. I put my hands over my face. I started crying and couldn't stop. The others woke up, laid their hands on my back. No one was alarmed. Crying spells happened. When my tears finally stopped, hours later, I got up and began to walk. The others watched me go. They understood.

I walked to our old neighborhood, down our street filled with narrow brick rowhouses and skinny trees propped up with plastic and wire. I stood in front of our old house. The blinds were drawn, the door shut. On the street, I spotted the silver Honda Accord Greg and I used to share. I placed my hands on the window, peered inside. The car, as always, was neat as a pin, not a scrap of paper or empty coffee cup in sight. Greg used to vacuum the interior every weekend, wipe the dashboard with a cloth. Everything was just the same – except now, in the back, sat a baby car-seat.

I stared at the car-seat. Then I dropped to my knees, my palms still pressed against the window.

'Greg!' I cried.

Coming from my mouth, his name sounded like a moan, a keen.

From the house – my old house – a flicker of movement. A face – oval, female, unchanged – appeared in the window, before the curtain was redrawn. I imagined this woman, the new wife, calling Greg, telling him to alert the police, that there was a Neanderthal loitering outside. I imagined Greg shaking his head, saying, *No, no, she's harmless; let her be*. I imagined the new wife cradling an infant to her chest, its soft head nestled under her chin, and saying, *But Greg, the baby*.

From where I knelt next to the car, I could see a chunk of concrete, a cracked piece of sidewalk come loose, lying near the curb. The city was always late in fixing things like this, I remembered. Used to drive me crazy. I got to my feet and reached for the concrete. I hefted the slab in my hand, ran my fingers along its rough edge, pressed my palm against its jagged point. Then I lifted the concrete and slammed it down on Greg's windshield.

'I'm sorry,' I cried, as the glass shattered and the car alarm wailed. But from my mouth, the words came out sounding like a roar.

EILEEN O'DONOGHUE

The Sound of the Summer

DAY 62

'Is he dead, Mam?' Ella appears in the kitchen in her pyjamas, rubbing her eyes awake.

'No, pet. He's still there, the poor boy.'

Her mother fills the kettle at the old belfast sink. Watching the jet of water, Ella considers the things she knows for certain. Her name is Ella Forde. She is twelve years old. It's day sixty-two of the hunger strike and she has five more days to deal with the nun.

'It's May Day,' she says, 'We could ask for a miracle.'

'Ella, please.'

'But why can't they do something?'

'It's too late, darling. Even if they could stop him.'

'That Thatcher is a dying bitch.'

'And where did you hear that kind of language, Miss? Have you been down in the shop with Mary?'

'I like Mary. She talks about things.' Mary also says shit and fuck-it-anyway and bastarding-bollocks-of-a-thing when she's trying to cash up the till, but Ella keeps that to herself.

'A load of old guff is what she talks, I don't know why your father puts up with her.'

'She brings the country people into the shop.' Ella replies.

'And that's more of it. Why do you know these things? It's not normal.'

'I'm going to get dressed.'

In the hall, she hears her mother, 'What about your breakfast?' then, 'Get clean socks out of the hot press' and 'Your flowers for the May altar are on the hall table.'

Racing across the footbridge, Ella remembers the blasted flowers and spots a colony of pale, lilac buds growing at the gates of the town park. She bends low and her schoolbag hits her in the back of the neck as she grabs fistfuls of them. Straightening herself, she pulls up her knee socks, and starts back over the bridge. The heron is in the river, standing in the bubbling water below the little weir. Broken rays of sunlight pierce through the overhanging trees touching the water all around her, like a wand dropping diamonds. Somewhere in the tall trees are eggs ready to

91

hatch. She waves at the heron, then clutching her small bouquet she runs across Church Street and in the gates of the Convent of Mercy, as the school bell strikes nine.

The entire school is gathered in the yard, at the statue of Our Lady. For Ella, these special morning prayers for the month of May mean half an hour less in Sr. Cassian's classroom. Last to join the line and squeezing in between two girls from her class, she avoids the nun's dark look.

Everyone else's flowers are already at the bottom of the statue of Our Lady. She puts her flowers behind her back but the girl next to her spots them and laughs, 'You're not serious!'

'What?'

'You know what they are, don't you?'

She doesn't answer, wants to defend her flowers but she can't.

'They're cuckoo flowers. You're not supposed to pick them. It's bad luck.'

'So, what happens if you do?'

'They cause a thunderstorm, stupid. And you get struck by lightning.'

'Is that all?' she laughs, pretending it's funny, but the small stems get hot and prickly in the palm of her hand. Five more days. She didn't mean to use up a miracle asking God to get rid of Sister Cassian. She's not sure how bad a procedure is but the nun is going to hospital for one and they're getting Mrs. Twomey, the sub, for the last few weeks before the summer holidays. She'll give them columns of maths to do while she's eating Mars bars and reading her Mills & Boons. Mary in the shop reads them too.

There's a hushing and Sr. Paul starts singing, *May is the month of Mary, month we all love so well, Mary is God's own mother. Gladly her praises we tell.* They say a decade of the rosary before Sister Angelo asks for special intentions. Ella wants two things. She wants to stay outside for a few more minutes and she wants to pray for the hunger strikers. Shaking a little from speaking in front of everyone, she asks, 'Sister, can we pray for Bobby Sands, for God to receive his soul when he dies?'

Sister Cassian is at her side in an instant. 'Don't mind that, Sister,' she says, 'Please go ahead with the other intentions.' Since nobody else is asking for anything, Sister Angelo smiles, smoothing out the wrinkles in her round face and says, 'Well, we could pray for victims of hunger around the world, I suppose.' She looks back at the head nun.

Sister Paul raises a hand, 'It's no harm to address this subject,' she says, 'I don't know what you are being told in your own houses, but make no mistake, that man is going against God's wishes and taking his own life.' She looks around the assembled troop of navy-blue uniforms and red cardigans, 'That is a mortal sin. None of you are to pray for him. Is that clear?' She allows the instruction to sink in and finishes the prayers with a sour Hail Holy Queen. Sister Cassian starts rounding up her class and pushes Ella to the front of the group, speaking sharply into her ear, 'I will deal with you in my own classroom.'

Marched in front of the line of girls, Ella loosens her grip on the May-day flowers, dropping them behind her on the tarred yard to be trampled by the girls behind. The nun's thin fingers pinch her upper arm as she is hurried through the door. She wills herself not to cry, no matter what, and tries to stay on her feet as the nun quicksteps her down the narrow corridor. She does not protest. She knows better. The corridor is dim after the brightness outside and smells of Jeyes fluid and candles when they have been blown out. It is like a bad three-legged race and they almost collide at the door of the classroom before stopping abruptly next to the teacher's desk.

'You will sit there all day.' The nun is shaking with temper and bangs the Baba's Chair down next to her desk. Once, she sat there for a whole week, after that time her mother came in because of the nightmares. Her mother is happy that she fixed it, so Ella doesn't tell her much about school anymore.

'But first, you will write on the blackboard, 'I am a stupid and ignorant girl' as many times as it will fit. You will write this because it is true,' and leaning close into Ella's face, the spray of her temper hitting Ella's cheek, she says, 'I wouldn't expect any better from an adopted brat.'

Ella holds onto the chalk board at the base of the blackboard. She writes a sentence and then another. She writes the lines slowly, carefully, the powdery feeling of the chalk on her fingers matching the dryness in her throat.

DAY 63

'Is he dead?' she asks her parents who are sitting down to their breakfast, the table laden with porridge, softly boiled eggs and toast, yellow butter and a dish or marmalade sitting side by side on the linen tablecloth, the old china teapot letting little puffs of steam escape from the spout.

'No, love, he's not. Eat something and don't be fretting about things you can't help.'

'I'm not hungry.'

'Why didn't you have a bit of a lie-in?' asks her father, placing Saturday's Examiner on the table to the left side of his plate, one hand for the teacup and one hand for the paper.

'I wanted to know.'

The three of them sit in easy silence, Ella moving pieces of cereal around the milk in her bowl, her mother's pale, morning face distracted while she drinks her tea staring into the distance. Without looking, she knows her father is frowning and squinting at the small print of the paper. She knows he will read the sports page last and he will fold the paper and put it under his arm when he goes down to the shop. She knows that she is adopted, has always known that she was special because they picked her out to be their child, but the way the nun said it was different, like there was something wrong about what went before it.

Looking at the time, her mother starts to clear the dishes but her father, taking the cups from her hands, says, 'Go on to the hairdresser, love. I can hear Mary clattering around below and the shop will be quiet for a while yet.'

Her mother, pulling on her coat says, 'Are you sure? Thanks, love. As for you, Miss, stay up here out of Mary's way and do your homework.'

'What's it these days?' asks her father.

'Cuckoos,' Ella explains, 'We've to look them up in the encyclopedia for a project and hand it up on Tuesday.

'I see, and what do you know so far?'

'That they lay their eggs in another bird's nest and fly off leaving the other bird to do all the work.'

'Well yes, but don't be too hard on them. Aren't they just following their nature? We always loved the cuckoo's call because it was the sound of the summer.' And the two of them set about cleaning the kitchen together.

'Dad, will you put out a black flag when he dies?' She is drying plates and he is stacking them in the press.

'Your Mam would prefer I didn't.'

'Why?'

'It's a small town and that means not showing off your opinions.'

'But you're going to do it anyway?'

'Yes.' He leans a moment against the sink as the last cup is dried, then taking the cup from her, he places it the press, closing the door.

'Sister Paul said we are not to pray for him because he is taking his own life. She said it's a mortal sin.'

'Did she now?'

'She said he can't go to Heaven.'

'And she's in charge of who can go to heaven now, is she?'

'But is it true that he can't?'

'I don't believe that, love,' he says, putting a hand on her narrow shoulder.

'I'm glad, Daddy.' She casts her eyes down as they fill.

'Will you be alright with the cuckoos? It's about time I went downstairs. We'll hear Mary cursing up here in a minute if I delay any longer.' He rolls his eyes and mimics Mary as he goes out the door, looking over his shoulder to smile at her, forgetting his newspaper.

She lies on her stomach on the sitting room carpet, legs crossed behind her, toes pointing to the ceiling. The Encyclopedia Britannica is open on the rug in front of her and beside it, open at P, their ancient dictionary, its pages yellow and dry. So far, she has read, *the cuckoos' contempt for the ordinary decencies of family life makes them pariahs.* The dictionary says, *Pariah, an outcast, one that is rejected and despised.* Back to the Britannica, she reads, *cuckoos spend the winter in Sub-Saharan Africa,* which is another thing she will have to look up, under S. She reads on. *During the weeks leading up to laying, females will have casual encounters with males, mating with several of them at the same time. Then as soon as the eggs are laid, the mother cuckoo grows a new set of feathers and leaves for Africa. The youngster will have to follow her on its own, the route being hardwired into its brain.'*

DAY 64

'What happened? Is it over?'

Ella wakes suddenly to find her mother pulling back the curtains at her bedroom window.

'You overslept, that's all.'

'He's not dead then?'

'No, pet. Get up and get ready for Mass. We'll pray for him there.'

'Okay, I'll be ready in a minute.' She stretches and pushes her hair back from her face. There are dust particles suspended in the rays of sunlight and little rainbows are cast on the wall through the crystal lamp on her dressing table. She opens the window to hear the rushing of the river behind the shop, pictures it between the two bridges, the only place where the river really belongs to the town.

When she is dressed, she opens her jewellery box. The ballerina sticks a bit sometimes when she is trying to turn, but the music still plays. She takes out her watch and bracelet, presents from her parents. The gold-plated bracelet has an oval, flat piece that sits on the back of her wrist with the word Ella engraved on it. In Irish, the word *eile* is said just like her name. They learned that it means *another.* The dictionary said *eile, other, different or strange."*

The church is packed for twelve o'clock Mass. Before the sermon, there is a hum of movement, a wave connecting the adults, then Ella feels a sudden stillness, a note of expectation. Father Walshe is speaking Bobby Sands words, measuring them out, emphasising each one.

'If I die, God will understand.' He says it slowly and clearly.

Taking off his reading glasses, he holds them high in one hand, facing the congregation. He is cross and red in the face and he has their full attention. 'If there is any doubt in this parish about the actions of the hunger strikers – if you are making a judgement that only God in his wisdom is entitled to do, then I say to you now, to close your mouth, and listen to these words again, 'If I die, God will understand', and I say to you that God does understand this solitary sacrifice. He will not forsake this man. He will not shut him out of his Kingdom.'

People are clapping, standing up. A few men are walking out, wives and children not sure if they should follow. A man at the top of the church is telling Father Walsh he is a disgrace to the church before making a show of walking down the long centre aisle. She cannot see into the nun's chapel at the side of the altar. Her mother stirs in her seat to look at her father who takes Ella's hand in his and she is suddenly on her feet, in an uprising surge of emotion that lasts long after the applause dies away.

DAY 65

'I don't want to go to school. I want to be here when he dies.' Ella is still in her pyjamas when her mother comes into her room to see if she is ready.

'You are going to school and that's that. Now, get out your uniform.'

'I won't be in the way. I can finish my project for tomorrow.'

'You going to school like a normal child instead of brooding here, like an old woman, about something you're too young to understand.'

I am not normal. I am eile.

'Can you tell me why you are so sad about it?'

'I'm sad because he is lonely,' she says, *Other – Noun, the other one, a member of a group that is perceived as different, foreign, strange.*

'He has his family and his priest,' says her mother, 'and the whole country is praying for him.'

'No,' she says, 'he is alone.'

The nun starts the day with an announcement. 'As tomorrow is my last day with you girls, we will finish with a showcase of our work.'

Their projects will be displayed on the back wall and a prize will be given for the best one. A rustle of excitement whispers around the class. This room, which has been her day-time prison since last September, is not laid out like the other classrooms. The desks are arranged in a U shape so the nun can see the face of every girl at the same time. She can see under their desks too, where the navy, carpet-tiles are to be kept completely free of clutter. Only their schoolbags, to be placed neatly on the left, are allowed on the floor.

Her eyes are closing in the afternoon heat. She tries to keep them open, but she cannot. She starts, shakes her head a little, barely aware of the nun talking about the French Revolution, walking behind the girls, looking over their shoulders at their copies. She cannot focus. She takes up her pen to try and stay awake, scribbling in dark ink on the corner of her history copy, *Day 65.*

She hears the whack before she feels it in the back of her head. Then pain is brief, a lightning flash, but she is winded, thinks she will vomit. Instinctively, she slides off her chair and curls up in a ball under her desk. But the nun is there, pulling her out, by the hair, by her cardigan, spitting, 'Come out here, you bold girl. Come out here this minute.' She has nothing to cling to and her knees burn against the rough carpet.

'Stand up!' screeches the nun. 'What's this? More of this carry-on out of you?' She grabs Ella's copy, tears out the page. 'You think that man is special and why? Because you think you are special. Well I'm here to tell you that you are nothing of the sort. Now, stand there and remain standing until home-time.'

She stands, on guard at first in case of another blow. But the nun has backed away and the others have bowed their heads, returning to the work. The clock over the blackboard says it is quarter to three. Fifteen minutes. Fifteen minutes and one more day. She leans for a moment, heavily on the cheap wooden desk. The looping pattern of the laminate blurs, then a single tear falls from her face on to the desk, spreading in a small, contained circle. She wipes it away with her sleeve.

DAY 66

'Get up! Get up!' Ella flicks on the light in her parent's bedroom.

'Are you sick?' Her mother sits up in the bed, blinking at the sudden brightness, reaches for her glasses.

'He's dead,' Ella says, 'Get up. Please!'

'What time is it?' her mother asks, still shielding her eyes from the light. Her father is finding his slippers with his feet at the other side of the bed, already understanding.

'How do you know, pet?' he asks, reaching for his old cardigan, thrown on the bedside chair.

'I brought the kitchen radio down to my room, after ye went to bed. Come on, please'

'Was it just now?' asks her mother.

'At seventeen minutes past one,' she says, 'Hurry on. It's going to be on the television.'

They sit together watching the special report, Ella and her mother in their dressing-gowns, her father's house-cardigan over his pyjamas, her mother crying quietly at times, the yellow bulb hanging from the ceiling under its old purple shade, giving out a ghost light in the bruising darkness of the early morning.

Her mother is filling the kettle for the umpteenth time. It is almost eight and they have slept in fits and starts.

'Maybe you should stay at home today.'

'No, I'll be okay.'

'But you're up all night. You'll be worth nothing.'

'I'm alright, Mam. Where's Dad?'

'Putting his flag out, for all the good it will do him. Did you know he got two, one for the shop and one for up here? Thanks be to God, I persuaded him one was enough. People might overlook one.'

'What did he do with the other one?'

'I put it in the hot press where he won't look for it.'

Excitement builds as the presentations begins. The back wall of the classroom is a sea of bright posters covered in hand-written information and pasted on cut-out pictures. Each girl in her turn, stands by her project, giving a self-conscious little speech. Ella is at her desk watching a small brown bird on the windowsill, his chirrups coming through the top windows which are open like envelopes. She recognises the skylark by the little tuft on his head. The room is warm and stale, the afternoon air already used by everyone.

For the first time all day, Sister Cassian speaks to her. 'Your project, please. Have you finished it?'

'Yes,' she answers flatly, not looking at her.

'Yes, what?' says the nun, demanding her title.

'Yes, Sister,' she says, reaching into her bag, for the rolled-up flag.

It is five minutes to three as she pins the black flag to the wall amid intakes of breath and nervous whispering. In the centre, stabbed with a single pin, is a page of plain white paper. On it, clear black words.

Cuckoos are the sound of the Summer.

Thirty girls hold their breath. They know one thing for certain. Ella Forde is in trouble now. Sister Cassian turns her back to them and walks to her desk in pronounced steps. She checks the clips at the back of her veil with her white fingers, then smooths her full black skirt. She is in no hurry. She gets the baba's chair from the corner, puts it next to her desk. She does it lightly, calmly, before sitting down to face the room again.

'You see, girls' she says, waving her hand in the direction of the posters, 'All of these projects are informative and well presented. But this feeble effort, this excuse for a piece of work, does not belong with the rest of them.' To Ella she says, 'Take it down. Now.'

Ella unpins the flag and bundles it roughly in her arms, hugs it close to her.

'You will sit here,' the nun says, 'It might be home time but you're not going anywhere.'

She picks up her schoolbag and slings the strap over one shoulder, looking for the bird. His eyes are tiny black dots. He is puffing himself up, getting ready to take off. He shrugs his feathers and begins to sing in one loud note. She keeps the flag close, folded in her arms, in front of her. The girl's heads are bent together in pairs, whispering until they go quiet and watch her from uniform eyes.

As the clock strikes three, Ella Forde stops for a moment at the blackboard. She touches the dusty chalk board, slides her finger along the grooves where the chalk fits, gathering dust on her fingertips. She traces the dust along the top of the baba's chair, but she does not sit there. She looks again for the skylark. He is a speck now, a blink in the distance, high up in the immense blue, but she can still hear his long, clear note.

DHYANNA RAFFI-DAVID

Gia's Midsummer's Eve

Janelle and Kailene leapt on the bed, and the folded baby clothes bounced.

'*We're your backyard friends,*' they sang jumping to the PBS kid-show music, '*the Back-Yard-uh-Gaaans!*'

'I'm Uniqua,' said Janelle.

'I'm Tasha,' said Kailene.

'I'm Angry,' I said, 'if you mess up my laundry.'

They shrieked with laughter and grabbed each other's hands. Lukas looked up from his crawl-position on the floor. His blue Thomas Train had provided a full five minutes of baby-happiness, but the bed-jumping was sure to prompt tears of frustration and envy. He struggled to his feet, clinging to the bed frame and reaching toward his sisters.

'Look,' cried Janelle, pointing at the window, 'a birthday party!'

The girls bounded off the bed and ran to the window, which had just been fitted with safety-locks four days earlier. As all the bedrooms were on the second floor, and as we had three small children who liked to climb, jump, and cartwheel, children who might go skull cracking, bone-crushing, body boomerang-ing down to the pavement the moment a parent wasn't looking, we had the entire townhouse safety-proofed the minute we moved in.

Our new home was the back unit, attached by one common wall to the front unit. Neither townhouse had a yard, the front was graced with a jacaranda tree and some sidewalk roses, our unit boasted a bougainvillea vine and potted pansies on the front step. The adjacent property had a large yard, three times the size of the tiny house which slouched at the front end of it. There, in the wide expanse of weeds that filled the lot from fence to fence, a card table fluttered with blue and white crepe paper streamers. A bright turquoise-colored cake shone in the sun, a helium balloon blazoned with 'Happy Birthday!' bobbed above it, and just beyond, a gaggle of kids rode bicycles and skateboards in a circle around a large slab of concrete that might once have been the foundation of a garage, now long gone.

The girls raced down the stairs, flew out the door, and spilled into our driveway as I scooped Lukas up and dropped him in the playpen. As I threw open the door I found the girls straddling the top of the stucco wall.

'What did I tell you about climbing that?' I hurried to the wall and reached up for Kailene.

'We're just watching,' Janelle said.

A thin dark-haired woman walked over to the wall, cigarette in hand, and said, 'You want some birthday cake?'

The girls nodded.

'Then get the hell down from there and join the party.'

The girls grinned and leapt down from the wall into her yard, running straight for the cake table. 'You too,' the woman said, blowing out a long trail of smoke into the air above us, 'I'm Gia. Walk around to the front door. Bring your little one.'

I hurried back inside, picked up Lukas, slung my diaper bag over my shoulder, and clunked down the driveway. Gia's front door was wide open, and when I stepped inside, a few men were sitting in the living room drinking beer and watching the USC-UCLA game. Strapped into a car seat positioned in front of the widescreen slept a baby with a forgotten, half-empty milk-bottle leaking into his diaper. A Viking—he sported a blond beard and a ring in his nose—motioned me to walk through. 'Tell Gia I'll be out in a minute,' he said. I thought that was unlikely.

The house was even tinier on the inside than it looked from the outside, I could only see entries to two bedrooms as I moved through the walkway, it wasn't really a hall, to the small yellow-tiled kitchen. The breakfast counter, which was currently a computer desk, was stacked neatly with invoices and receipts. The dishes and glasses were lined up, perfectly spaced, on the open-faced shelves, and the pots hung from hooks on the ceiling, according to size. I walked through to the back step where Gia was sitting, watching the kids eat cake as they jumped in and out of a kiddie pool filled with balloons.

She offered me a joint.

I shook my head.

'You one of them poison-free, straight-edge, vegan people?'

'No. It makes me cry. Every time I smoke dope I cry. If you give it to me, you'll take it away in five minutes and say, "Yeah, this isn't for you".'

She nodded and pulled out her thermos. 'Margarita.'

'Sure.'

She poured some into a plastic party cup and handed it to me.

'I made it from fresh limes,' she said. 'Got the recipe from the Las Fogatas restaurant. It's authentic.'

'Perfect,' I said. And it was.

The kids were now playing nerf gun tag, the orange bullets flying across the yard, and Gia had to periodically stand up, clap her hands and call 'time out' so both teams could pick up ammo and reload. She had six kids under age eight, two for every one of mine. 'I don't know how you do it,' I said.

'Same as you,' she said, 'only with less sleep and more screaming.'

Lukas crawled up and down the one stair. 'The camper,' I said—pointing to a rusted-out camper-trailer sitting in the weeds, 'you go out on the trail with all these kids?'

'Hell no,' she said. 'My in-laws parked that here four years ago and it's never moved, it just gets rustier. The kids aren't allowed inside. Gordy uses it as his man-cave. When his nerves get fried, I send him out there. There's a TV and a boom box over the bed.'

'Home away from home,' I said.

'Something like that,' she poured herself some margarita. 'Hey Caleb.' She stood up again. 'Stop hitting your brother!'

'He's just mad he fell down again,' the brother, Cory, retorted, poking Caleb in the gut, 'Klutz!'

'No hitting. You okay Caleb? It's his birthday.' She sat down.

I made a mental note—purchase a gift. 'How old?' I asked.

'Eight.'

'My oldest is seven.'

'Second grade then. Mrs. Cartwright? She's a good teacher.'

There was a large, dilapidated sign leaning against the wall, *Gordan's Construction* it said, though the letters had begun peeling off.

'Gordan's,' I said. 'That name sounds familiar,' but I was lying, it was an ice-breaker maneuver.

'Gordy's going to repaint it and put it back up when he gets his business going again. We did construction.' She wriggled her toes in her flip flops, and absently picked at her big toe where the black nail-polish was chipping away. 'Speaking of which, your place is brand new,' she tilted her head toward our condo. 'Built by our competitor. How do you like it?'

I wasn't sure what the right answer was. 'It's great to be a homeowner,' I said, 'First time for us.'

'Lots of house to keep clean.'

'Yeah.' I looked at our townhouse looming over the wall. From here it looked like a white, Spanish-tiled mansion gleaming in the sun. Although it was tall and skinny, it had four bedrooms and 2,400 square feet.

'You got a maid?'

I shook my head.

'Ah, you do it all yourself.' She leaned her head back, took another hit, her eyes momentarily closing. 'I like that.' When she'd fully exhaled she said, 'Your neighbor up front?'

'Snob,' I said.

She laughed. 'Can you believe she calls her husband *Taylor Number Two*?'

I grinned. 'He puts up with it.'

Kadim and I had moved into the neighborhood knowing it was on the upswing. My father had told us to buy quick while the getting was good. Multi-unit dwellings were rising like wildflowers across the open lots of newly deceased landowners. They died, left their homes to their kids, who promptly sold them to a rich developer who papered the area with fliers, offering cash for old houses. The land parcels were large, the houses were tiny. From my master bedroom I looked down mostly on Gia's yard. Her home sat far forward on the lot, its grey, tar-shingled roof slumped in the middle, like an old mare with a sway back, and the peach tree by the garage dropped all its fruit while it was still green. There was the lime tree next to it, and you could hardly tell the difference between the limes and the peaches lying on the ground. For coastal Southern California, where property was at a premium, large lots like these were gold mines, even, if like Gia's, they were landscaped with nothing but crabgrass and dandelions. Only a year ago, ours had probably looked just the same.

In contrast to Gia, my front townhouse neighbor, Thalia, blonde, elegant, and an active alumnus of USC's Kappa Alpha Theta chapter, was hard at work upgrading her already beautiful brand-new unit. She had invited me over for drinks the day we moved in, and her mother was there, helping select wallpaper. The samples were neatly arranged on the buffet. Thalia liked the pastel colors, but her mother wanted a traditional rose pattern. I was careful to voice no opinion when asked.

Thalia served Cosmos shaken over ice. 'It was smart of you to give your kids American names,' she said as she handed me my martini glass. 'You know if you name them things like DeShawn and LaQuisha they will never get jobs.' As she lifted the rose-colored glass to her lips, her squared-off salon nails gleamed. Maybe she took the Cosmo to the salon to match the color. 'It's a documented fact those resumes get thrown out. But you're white,' she said, 'so you know better.'

The mother proved to be the wiser of the two, she kept silent. After Thalia's second drink, the true purpose of her invitation shifted into focus. 'I've written a letter to the city,' she said. 'I've asked them to condemn the house next door. The landlord will either have to fix it up or sell it. Probably in this market he'll sell it. It's big enough for two, maybe even three condos.'

I set my drink down. 'I don't really know,' I said, trying to make my voice more soothing than it sounded in my head, 'We're so new here. It's too soon to get involved in neighborhood politics.'

Thalia waved her hand, her drink sloshed in the delicate glass. 'Seize the day,' she said.

Inwardly I cringed. 'To be honest, I'd rather look at the weeds than at someone else's bedroom window. One of the reasons we bought the place was because there was a mostly open lot next door. It's like being next to a field of unmown grass.'

'You can't be serious,' she said. 'It's a dump.'

She offered a silver platter of goat cheese on water crackers. 'It would help if you would write a letter as well. There's power in numbers.'

I smiled.

'Please, take one,' her mother said of the crackers.

'You know her house makes your property value go down,' Thalia continued. 'If you play your cards right, you can move out of this condo in three to five years, and you could land someplace really nice. Think about the long game, think about equity.'

Her mother poured a second drink. She stood, leaning over to top off mine.

'No thanks,' I said, putting my hand over my glass. I had not rushed a sorority at college, and at just that moment I was remembering why.

Thalia's husband popped his head in the doorway and waved. 'Hi, I'm Taylor.'

'Hi,' I said. 'I'm Esme.'

'He's my second Taylor.' Thalia smiled and waved back at him.

'*Taylor Number Two*,' Gia said, 'because she dated a *Taylor Number One* before him. Did she tell you that story?'

I laughed.

Gia blunted the joint on the step and put it in her shirt pocket. 'I wonder how it feels being reminded every goddam day of your life that your wife banged someone else before you.'

It was true, you could hear Thalia calling her husband from the doorstep, '*Taylor Two*, can you close the garage door?' and '*Taylor Two* can you wind up the hose?'

'I don't know, but from the way he looks at her, you can tell he thinks he won a prize; that he'd put up with just about anything to keep her happy,' I said.

'Yeah, that'll change.' Gia got up and stepped over to the crepe-paper table, procuring us two paper plates of cake. She was really thin, her stomach so flat it almost curved inward, and her skimpy tee-shirt barely covered her jutting hips. I wondered how that tiny frame had delivered six babies. Bodies are wondrous things. Hers was a rack of bones.

She put a spoonful of blue frosting in her mouth. 'High maintenance is like a toll road, you know? You get tired of paying the price every day, and you find another way home. I give them five years.'

'She doesn't plan to be in the neighborhood that long,' I said.

'Doesn't matter,' she said. 'He'll leave, you'll see.'

Lukas started to cry. I picked him up and bounced him on my knee, gave him his pacifier, but he spit it out and wailed. All my cooing and singing didn't bring the decibel level down.

'I've got a blanket,' Gia said, 'just did the laundry.' She ran inside and came out with a beach towel, and we spread it on the ground. I laid Lukas down on his back, but when he looked up at the blue sky, he only howled louder. I opened my diaper bag and pulled out the plush train, I stroked his face and started to sing the Thomas song, but it didn't help.

'Yeah, he's done for the afternoon,' Gia said. 'Go ahead, take him home. I'll send your other kids over when they've burned themselves out.'

'Are you sure?' I said. 'That's so many kids to watch.'

'Pffft,' she waved her hand. 'I've handled more than this.'

When I left, I had a pleasant buzz going, and true to her word, Gia sent my kids home exhausted.

Over the weeks, Gordy taught my daughters how to skateboard, and how to hammer a nail. Gia taught them how to play Mortal Kombat. I showed her kids how to make chocolate chip cookies and how to melt crayons onto craft paper to create homemade gift-wrapping. At my condo we made pinwheels. At Gia's house the kids popped wheelies.

'You're getting awfully close to that neighbor,' Kadim said. 'Don't you think it would be a better idea if you spent some time with Thalia?'

'Why? Because she's a Theta?'

'She has connections. And she knows what's what around town.'

'She's insufferable.'

'She might know someone who could throw me some business.'

'You talk to her then. Besides, Gia and Gordy help me, they are part of my team.'

'That's because Gordy's always home,' he said. 'I work.'

'I'll take what I can get.'

One afternoon I bumped into Thalia in the driveway while I was walking the kids over to Gia's. 'You going over there again?' she asked. 'You seem close.'

'We're friends,' I said, suddenly realizing Thalia was watching my daily treks to Gia's house through her window.

'She has kids I s'pose.' Thalia's mouth turned downward. 'A lot. Six to be exact.'

'Yes,' I said, 'she has her hands full.'

'We haven't been able to get pregnant.'

'I'm sorry.' I knew I should feel sorry for her, but I didn't.

'We're seeing an infertility doctor,' she offered.

I paused. Maybe she was trying to reach out. I thought about comforting her, I thought about telling her that we had also seen an infertility doctor, that it had been a hard time for us, that we had persevered, that it had all been worth it. For a moment I considered sharing infertility information, maybe bonding, maybe even setting the stage to win a client or two for Kadim, but I decided against it. I didn't trust her with my personal information. I didn't trust her at all.

'I wish you the very best of luck,' I said.

Every afternoon Gia and I took the little ones for a walk in the strollers, sometimes to the park, but always across the boulevard into the rich neighborhood that bordered ours. The walks were so long I often had to sit Kailene on the stroller canopy, where she would lean into me and fall asleep.

'Why do you like to walk over here so much?' I asked.

'Wanna show them fancy folk what real people look like,' she said. Then she shrugged. 'Gordy helped build a lot of these houses. I like to look at them and say in my head, hey motherfucker, you think you're all that?—I built your house. Caleb!'

Caleb, who had a bandage on his forehead, and who always exhibited a certain youthful gawkiness, although he was the best skateboarder of the bunch, took an odd, twitchy sidestep, and fell into the street. He didn't cry, but he laid there a minute, dazed. Kailene helped him up.

'Caleb?' Gia raced over to him, frustrated.

'I'm ok,' he said, but he seemed disoriented, and both knees were bloody. I pulled out a baby-wipe and started cleaning his knees, Gia stroked his hair. He was a sweet kid, with long silky black hair that was always falling into his big blue eyes.

'I got Band-Aids,' I said, digging into my bag.

'Nah.' He started to get up, 'no Band-Aids.'

'Bactine,' I sprayed the antibacterial on his scrapes and watched as he squinted against the sting.

'I'm good,' he said, taking a tentative first step, then walking slowly with Kailene.

'I don't know what's wrong with that kid,' Gia said, nervously lighting another cigarette, 'he's gotten so clumsy lately.'

'He's a boy,' I said. 'They do dumb stuff.'

She took a long drag. 'Even the boys in these rich houses do dumb stuff. Right?'

'Right. Dumb and rich are not mutually exclusive. Just cuz you're rich doesn't mean you're smart.' I pointed to a house that had both a white and a black Porsche in the driveway. 'Doesn't it make you feel a little weird to see so many high-priced coaches sitting in a row? I feel like I'm walking through a Modern American version of Downton Abbey. Where's the paid driver?'

'I like to imagine living here sometimes,' she said, pushing the stroller forward on the sidewalk, 'I like to think about having a maid. Someone to help with the laundry.'

From my bedroom I could not only see Gia's house, but I could hear her washer and dryer going 24/7. Sometimes I would go over and help her fold. Her baby slept in the master bedroom in a crib, the other kids shared a room with bunk beds, and trundles. They kept their clothes in a stack of plastic containers from Target—each one a different color. We would fold and put the clothes into the boxes. By the next day, there were entire loads ready to fold again. And bed sheets. And towels. And Gordy's work clothes when he picked up work.

But he didn't pick up much work, and I began to notice Gia's mood darkening. She smoked more, laughed less. She seemed to get thinner, if that was possible. Somedays when I came over, she hadn't washed the clothes at all, she was just sitting in the living room playing Donkey Kong, surrounded by empty potato chip bags. When I went in the kitchen, there were piles of dishes in the sink.

'Don't you hate washing dishes?' she said, not moving from her seat on the couch. 'You do them, and three hours later, there's more to do, and then three hours after that, there's even more to do. I can't run the dishwasher at the same time as the washing machine. It uses all the water.'

'It's the myth of Sisyphus,' I said, turning on the tap.

'Huh?'

'The task that never gets done. It's one of Satan's tortures in hell.'

'Right,' she said. 'Hell.'

'Just relax,' I said, 'I've got it.' I filled the sink and plunged my hands into the soapy water. When I'd dried the last dish, I loaded piles of dirty clothes into a laundry bag. 'I'll take them to my house to wash,' I said.

She started to cry.

I sat down next to her.

'What's wrong?'

She waved her hands at the mess, at the backdoor where the kids were playing outside with the nerf guns, at the empty Little Caesar's pizza box on the coffee table. 'Gordy hasn't found work,' she said, her breath whistling through her now snuffly nose, 'I'm going to have to try to get my dental hygienist job back. What am I going to do, leave him in charge of all this?'

I had wondered for a while how they'd been getting by, and specifically how they had lost Gordy's business. I knew they'd been renting their house for at least four years, and from what I could piece together, at some point, Gordy had owned a construction business, his cousin had managed the books, and somehow the cousin had underpaid the taxes, for so long that when they got audited, they couldn't see any way out of the hole they were in. They gave up the business rather than slave to save it. I wasn't sure it made sense, but then I wasn't sure it made any sense to them. I wasn't sure they understood what had happened to them. Now Gordy hired himself out to other people.

'It'll work out,' I said, patting her knee. I figured he was in the camper, getting high.

'But things don't just work out,' she said. 'They get worse.' Her lungs heaved with a coarse gasp.

'What do you mean?'

'Caleb.'

'What about him?'

'He fell again. He hit his head hard. We took him to the hospital and they wanted to run some tests on him. Now they've told us his gait is so weird because he has Friedreich's Ataxia, this degenerative muscle thing. It's genetic.'

'Oh my God,' I said.

'I came all the way out here from New York at age twenty-one. I met a California guy, married him, and somehow, me from the east, and him from the west, who never met each other until ten years ago, it turns out we both have this rare gene, and we gave it to our kid, and when you have a gene from both parents, you get this disorder. You get the disease.'

I tried to think of her kids, if any others of them had the weird gait. But I stopped myself. *Deal with the issue at hand* I told myself.

'I'll babysit,' I said, 'and I'll help with the doctor's appointments. How else can I help?'

'No one can help,' she said. 'He's going to be in a wheelchair before he's fifteen.

'That can't be true.'

'It's true. There's no cure.' She lit a cigarette. 'The world doesn't make any sense. And things don't get better.'

I rubbed her back. My mind reeled. Gordy needed to step it up. I didn't know in what way, but he had to. Gia couldn't do much more.

'We're gonna find a way through this,' I said.

'I don't know,' she said, wiping her eyes, 'sometimes I just don't know.'

I went over later with dinner and the clean, folded clothes. I saw the notice from the city on the coffee table. 'What's this?' I picked it up.

She lit a joint. 'I have to give it to the landlord. Do you think he'll sell the property out from under us? I don't even have enough money to put down a deposit somewhere else.'

'He won't,' I said, 'He's held onto the property this long, it's earning him income. And it's not a condemnation notice, it's just a notice that there's been a complaint. Maybe he'll fix things up a bit.'

'Not likely,' she said. 'I have to hope the motherfucker doesn't die.'

Saturday afternoon I packed lunch for everyone into a picnic basket, and we walked to the park. Once we had the blanket spread out, the kids clambered onto the swings, and the little ones fell asleep in the strollers.

Gia said, 'Thalia invited me to a Midsummer's Eve party.'

'You going?'

We had received the same invitation. It was printed on cardstock from Christie's, the stationer's store in the next town over. At the top there was a little engraved graphic of a sun and moon shining over a squiggly-line ocean. Kadim and I were discussing the politics of going versus not going. The party was being held at the beach, at sundown, which would be about 8:30 pm.

'I don't even know what Midsummer's Eve is.'

'It's the longest day of the year,' I said. 'I guess it's big over in Europe. They light bonfires, they get drunk, they walk on embers.'

'Bonfires,' she repeated.

'Yeah, you know, burn out the old, clear space for the new. You walk on the embers to experience Mind Over Matter. Fire walking.'

'Who wants to celebrate the longest day of the year?' she said.

'I don't know. Thalia. Remember Daisy in the Great Gatsby?'

It suddenly occurred to me that was exactly who Thalia looked like, Mia Farrow's Daisy Buchanan. Except she was mean. 'Daisy says, 'I always wait for the longest day of the year and then miss it.' I think here in the states we just miss it.' I remembered in the novel that Daisy snuffed out a candle with her fingers when she said that line, and it always seemed strange to me that such a slight fluttery-white-moth of a woman put her fingers to the flame. But I figured it was symbolic. She couldn't stand up for her lover, she just lit his flame, then doused him. She was a candle snuffer.

'The beach. At night. Is she kidding? With six kids and no lifeguard? My idea of hell.'

'Mine too,' I said.

'Gordy still has some Mexican fireworks leftover from last summer.'

'Kinda illegal,' I said.

She shrugged. 'No one's ever stopped us. We light them every year.'

I thought of Thalia, but then, she'd be at the beach.

'Let's have our own party,' I said.

'Done,' she said.

But every time I talked to Gia about the party, she got a faraway look in her eyes.

'I'll pay for everything,' I said. 'You just provide the backyard.'

'Okay,' she said.

'Fireworks?'

She nodded.

I talked to Gordy about barbecuing and he was onboard. Kadim said he'd help, although he and Gordy had never bonded much. 'You can watch sports together,' I said.

'I hate baseball,' he said.

'You can do it,' I said. 'There's not that much we can do for them, this is a small thing.'

He took my hands. 'I don't mind doing it, I don't mind you doing it. But you have to realize we have problems too, and your energy is better spent here.'

I looked around the room. 'I don't see anyone suffering from neglect.

'Just keep it in mind. You can't save people.'

'I'm not trying to save Gia, I'm trying to create a few points of brightness in a dark life.'

'It's not going to work, and it's not enough. Try to keep an even keel is all.'

I marinated pork ribs and made coleslaw. I bought hotdogs and hamburger meat, buns and chips. I made lemon cupcakes and decorated them with moons and stars. I cut out sugar cookies in the shapes of suns and the kids frosted them in fiery shades of yellow and orange. We placed them on a tray, so it looked like the blazing suns slowly moved from orange to yellow to pale evening moons and stars midway through the lineup. I went to the Dollar Store and got squirt guns for a water fight, fruit flavored lollipops for a lollipop hunt, and zinnia seeds to plant in tiny clay pots — an homage to the oncoming summer.

When I pulled out the folding tables from the garage, they were dusty, so I recruited all the kids to help soap them down and rinse them with the hose. We dried them off with rags in the warm sunshine of the driveway.

Kadim was at work, so I decided to carry the tables over myself. I set the kids up with pretzels in front of the TV to watch *Bob the Builder*. 'I'll be back in one second.'

But when I got to Gia's driveway carrying the first table, I could smell smoke.

I dropped the table and ran to the backyard.

She was standing near the camper, holding a lighter fluid can and smoking a cigarette. In the middle of the yard, in a giant dirt hole, a bonfire raged. Every item of apparel the family owned, pants, shirts, pajamas, underwear was roaring in the blaze, smoking, twisting.

'Gia!'

She turned to me. The clothes contorted in the flames.

'What are you doing!'

'Laundry,' she said, turning back toward the fire, her face glowing in the torrid light.

I saw her standing, a gaunt shadow in front of the raging blaze, her long black hair flickering and waving in the heat, and my heart stopped.

I raced toward the flames, grabbed her arms, and pulled her into my chest, walking backward, one frail frame wrapped up in a stronger frame, moving in reverse as a solid unit, together, our feet on the ground, returning to the bicycles, returning to the skateboards and stroller, back towards the garden hose and the kiddie pool, and back toward Gordy. I heard a wail, but it wasn't her sobbing.

It was me.

I had grabbed her before she could be swallowed by the flames, before she could dissipate like a vapor into that intensifying heat.

The Entomologist's Pin

You'll be thinking I stole that car. I didn't. I may be a criminal, but truly I have never stolen a damn thing in my whole entire life. Fact is, that car was mine. A present from Leo given just after we were married. A yellow Volkswagen Beetle. I guess that was supposed to be funny. Or cute. Who knows? It arrived much like him, unexpected, unreliable, a little shabby and from England.

He made a big show of handing me the keys, all mounted up with pins in a shadow box, like one of his butterflies. Tell the truth, I would have preferred one of his specimens as a gift.

'What's this?' I asked as he sat there, cross legged on the end of my bed in a pair of those striped cotton pjs you only ever see on network repeats of *Leave It To Beaver*.

'Open it.' He said, all grasshopper-eyed and bristly with excitement. So I did.

'Are those keys? I can't tell. Can you hand me my glasses?' I don't see much without them.

'Ah yes, but keys for what?'

'No clue,' I said and I put the box to one side because just then I only wanted my glasses, my book, and the tea he'd made for me.

'Well? Aren't you going to ask me?'

'Murderation, Leo! It's not a quarter of seven even.'

'Oh now, don't be so grumpy!' He was off the bed, pulling at my hand to follow him. He guided me downstairs and led me outside, still in my nightshirt, covered my glasses with hands that felt warm and soft on my face like poached fruit.

'It's a surprise, and I know, I know how you loathe them. But you're going to love this one!'

He was wrong.

Were you ever with someone who was just happy all the time? You know, constantly buoyant, perky, content. That sound appealing to you? Well, it's not. It's exhausting. Suffocating, is what it is. That was Leo. Easy to love and hard not to hate. The relentless, heartless damned optimism of him.

He released his hands, gestured grandly and I saw that car, The Beetle, sitting by the sidewalk, more or less where I found it this morning.

'It's a car.'

'No darling, it's your car. All yours.'

'Mine?' I asked and what I meant to ask was *what do I want with a car? I cycle everywhere. I like cycling. I don't need that car. I don't want that car.* Instead I thanked him and there it sat for the next six weeks until a day came when he took the keys and started driving the damned thing himself. I only ever drove it that one time, twenty years back, and that was to push it off a cliff.

So yes, it was a shock when it turned up this morning. I quite literally did not see it coming. Sure, there are big windows out front of the house, but the glass is mostly frosted. Direct sunlight damages Leo's specimens. Fades their wings and dries their little bodies to dust. Some of them, the older ones, are now barely more than the odd leg, antenna or costa poking out from tiny piles of powder in the bottom of a shadow box. Butterflies love the light when they're alive, but once they're dead and pinned in a case, it's a different story. The light does for them. Light is time and time is light, isn't that what Einstein said? Maybe I should've gotten drapes.

Soon as I saw that car this morning, two thoughts came up humming, butting like bluebottles: *it's back* and *that's not possible*. I'm not sure quite what I did next. Probably just stood there a while but eventually I opened the front door. Curiosity's obnoxious that way, like a fly, you just can't swat it down.

The car was empty. Driver's door a little open. Same plates, same seats, same keys left in the ignition. Same stink of warm plastic and stale cologne. Same nasty yellow car. Volkswagen called that colour Oriole. Another person on another day might have called it sunshine, dandelion or even a cadmium yellow. But for me this morning, it was guilty acid-reflux yellow, bilious insincerity yellow. No wait. This was retribution yellow.

A swarm of questions all flew out at once as just,

'Hello?'

I waited and I said it a couple more times and then added,

'Is anyone there?' like I was holding some sidewalk seance. No reply, just the ticking, cooling engine and the imagined gaze of my neighbours. I wanted to check under the hood in case the driver was in there and I didn't want to check under the hood in case the driver was still in there. A lean and silky spider was getting up a web on the side mirror. I let it crawl and then I crushed it.

I didn't realise he killed them until I got here and I saw how he worked. Sounds dumb, but I didn't think about where all the butterflies and moths came from. Turns out he raised them, *farmed them* he'd have said, from eggs. Out the back of his brownstone was this big old glass house, its windows filmed a steaming verdigris by waxy palms and curled and trembling ferns. Inside the green was jewelled with jasmine, mimosa and suicide trees. In there the wooly-soft air was lily-pungent with a tang of dank compost and overripe fruit. On a sunny day it glittered with wings. Tiger Swallowtails, barred and chalkboard creamy, iridescent Glasswings and heavy azure Blue Morphos that flopped around like small, drunk birds.

I loved to read in there, furl up in the tatty rattan armchairs until the heat made me saggy and the humidity dimpled my pages. Leo too. He kept this frumpy old gramophone in there that played breathy, woozy recordings of Lucienne Boyer through a curved and tarnished horn that skulked among the flowers like an ugly, tin hibiscus.

'Sorry about the din,' he said once. 'I rather feel like I should be wearing spats and serving us mint juleps. Not really my taste I'm afraid, but better than silence, eh?'

I didn't agree.

He'd lounge on a floor cushion, wilt across a chair, observe the butterflies. How they fed, how they flew. Sometimes he'd take photographs.

'Beautiful. Don't you think they're beautiful?' he'd ask, rarely expecting a response. One time I looked up and said,

'I guess. Sure are colourful.'

'Do you have a favourite?' he asked and dabbed at his forehead with a folded, pollen yellow handkerchief.

'No. Do you?'

'Yes, but it changes all the time.'

'Isn't that the same as not having a favourite?'

He blew his damp fringe off his face and looked puzzled, then he laughed.

'Do you know, I think you're right.'

'Don't it make you sad to kill them?' I asked him and for the longest time I thought he wasn't going to answer or maybe he hadn't heard me at all but then he said,

'Sad? No, not sad. It's preservation and preservation, my dear, is love at its most sincere. Everything fades away, my darling. Everything. No matter how lovely, no matter how perfect. But to catch what you love and to hold it there, in that moment of perfection, forever. That's an act of devotion, not destruction.' He stood up suddenly and reached for the soft net that leaned against the arm of his chair.

'That one,' he said and his fingers traced the looping path of a Swallowtail.

'How do you choose?' I asked. Now this was way back. Back when I still wore my hair long, and without dropping the net he came over to me. With his empty hand he lifted and smoothed a long strand of my hair through his fingers and he said,

'Oh, I always kill my favourite.'

I closed my book. I knew what came next. The capture, the kill, the artful arrangement of the little corpse with pins on the canvas.

'I'll go make some tea,' I said.

After Leo had gone, the glass house was still full of butterflies for a few beautiful months. I fed them fruit and kept them warm but I didn't know how to make them thrive. Turns out that killing the man who kills the butterflies doesn't save the butterflies.

I watched him work once. He had this long, wooden lab bench in his study, the kind that was popular in the thirties. At one end of the bench were piles of papers and photographs, diagrams and drawings, and manuscript notes on solvents, relaxants, degreasers and poisons. There were lamps and lenses of different strengths and pots filled with paint brushes, pipettes and pincers, and a pincushion prickling with varying lengths of pin.

He sat on a smooth wooden stool and I stood by a cluster of bottles and jars marked up with handwritten labels as chloroform, ether, carbon-tetrachloride, potassium cyanide and blue barber's gin. He was preparing a Madagascan Moon Moth he'd killed in the ice-compartment of our refrigerator. An insect don't feel pain in the way that we understand it, but that's the kindest way. They just fall asleep and die. If you've never seen a Madagascan Moon Moth, go ahead and Google it. They're big, bigger than your hand. Got these wide lime and lemon yellow wings that trail like the ribbons on a kite when they fly. Fuzzy chick-yellow body as thick as your thumb.

As Leo handled it, turned out he hadn't quite killed it enough and in his warm hands it began to come around. At first, I thought it was just Leo's breath moving over the antennae, but then it panicked and staggered over the desk in a scatter of long pins and pencils and Leo said,

'Oh Lord. He's waking up. Freezing should do the trick for these big buggers but this one's a bit...' he ran his hand through his hair, glancing around the bench, '...frisky.' He waved his other hand at me.

'Pass me the –' I handed him a kill jar but the moth flapped suddenly and he dropped it. He exhaled sharply.

'Bollocks. He'll bruise his hindwings and be completely unusable at this rate. I wouldn't normally do this but…' With one hand he caught and held the moth down and with the other used a long, fine pin to spear through the fluff at the back of its head. His strike was fatal before I could squint and say,

'Make it quick.'

The wings twitched and stilled. Leo reached for a magnifying eyepiece and leaned in close to the dead moth's head.

'Perfect. No one will ever know.'

I left the room after that, something stirred like a sediment in me. Excitement, titillation, apprehension? Maybe it was the chemicals. But I also wanted to retch and I never wanted to watch him work again.

I first met Leo in a lab at the Entomology Department in Cornell at the end of my PhD. He was a friend of my Professor and came in for some damn thing or other to do with a collection of Oleander Hawk Moths he was preparing for the faculty. I never really fell for him like he did for me. He was kind of odd ball, done up in a mustard bow tie and European cologne, wearing his old money like a holey tweed jacket.

My specialism was beetles, his was butterflies. My thing was conservation, his preservation. If you can call taxidermy that. We talked and we got on and I'd never really got on with a man in that way. I could tell you anything you'd care to know about the categorisation of the genus Coleoptera, but I knew nothing about all the other stuff. The bedroom stuff. My Dad used to joke, in a leery kind of way, to his friends at the bar, that I was at college studying the birds and the bees. I'd roll my eyes and pretend to carry on reading when they laughed but really it made me want to hit him with a chair.

So no, I didn't want to go back to living at Dad's when my studies ended. Dad was what he'd have called *a regular stand-up guy*. Loved the game on a Saturday, bathed and shaved on a Sunday. When I was home, he'd insist I come with to the bar when we both left work (his at the body shop, mine at Arby's), because *ya never know when ya gunna meet someone*. I never knew whether he meant for him or for me. But Dad was a welder and I was an entomologist. I liked to be alone, without his tv to numb and scatter my thoughts, without the stink of his smokes to haunt my books and papers. And let's face it, Wisconsin isn't the Upper West Side. I'd been offered a place at a lab, but I couldn't afford to rent alone. So when he asked, moving in with Leo was an easy decision.

Home for us was this brownstone he'd inherited from his Uncle. Must've been in the family for I don't know how long. There was something, maybe it's age or the dead grey light from those milky-blind frosted windows, or maybe the odour of acetone, ethanol and floor polish that made it feel, I don't know, museumy, a little institutional. Of course, I'd been to his house many times before but we weren't on what you'd call upstairs terms until the day I arrived with my neat vinyl Walmart suitcase and a carpet bag. I was a little surprised when it turned out that I wouldn't have my own room.

'Is it a problem?' he asked. 'Because I could certainly clear out dear old Eric's room for you. If you'd feel happier with that, I mean? I'm so sorry, I just assumed. How stupid of me.'

'It's cool,' I said. 'It just isn't how I'd envisaged things.'

'Funny girl!' he said and frowned and smiled at the same time. He said that often. He spent the night downstairs somewhere that first night, where exactly I couldn't say. The next day he cleared out his uncle's old room and it became mine. It stayed that way, even after we got married, except sometimes when we went up to bed and I said goodnight and he would say,

'Goodnight. Unless…'

'Unless what?' I said the first time.

'Well, unless you'd like to join me. In my bed. Unless you'd like to make love, perhaps?' I thought about it for a moment.

'Well alright, but I already took a Placidyl. Make it quick.'

I'd lie there, getting sleepy on the blank canvas of his sheets while he pricked and probed and performed the procedure. Maybe we made love or maybe we made nothing at all. Either way, we made no sense to me.

You'll be wondering about the Placidyl. It was no big deal. Back then everyone was taking something, right? I started taking Placidyl just after I moved in with Leo, before he started with all that bedroom business even. I was always a good sleeper and I'd got used to the city and I can tell you, even back then it was jungle-loud and thick with life's rich ripple all around the clock.

But there was this one night when something woke me. Do you remember that sound camera flash units used to make? That ascending-mosquito high whine as they charged and then the pop-click when they went off? It was that. I don't remember seeing the flash, although I'll bet that was part of it. When I opened my eyes, Leo was right there, sitting in the chair by my bed. In his hands was this old camera, some black bakelite thing with a stubby, brutish lens like a snout. I propped up on one arm.

'Smile for me,' he said. 'I want to remember.' I didn't smile. He did.

'Goodnight then,' he said and he left. If there were any photos, I never saw them. Never asked to. In the morning I found a long silver fixing pin on the chair where he had been sitting and the next night I started taking Placidyl.

It was easy in the end. One late afternoon, when Leo came in from the glass house with that Swallowtail he'd chosen, I emptied a few of those pretty green Placidyl capsules into his tea. He took plenty of sugar so there was no way he was going to taste it. I found him in the room he called the sitting room and I called the lounge, standing by the open French doors, a book in his hand but not reading. A waft of cut grass and diesel and soft frying onions, car horns and church bells and rows half in Italian, disco riffs and distant sirens, dog barks and close by us two booming pigeons, somebody singing and small children laughing and laughing. It all just drifted in. I handed him the teacup and he drank some right away. English people can do that with hot tea. He looked out into the garden.

'Lovely,' he said. 'Lovely cup of tea,' but then he put it down on a bookcase. 'Do you think -' he said and then he stopped and pressed the spine of the book to his lips.

'What?'

'Do you ever wish we'd had children?'

'No,' I said and then added 'Why, do you?' and tried to thaw the polar tones from my voice.

'Sometimes perhaps. On days like these, oh how can I put it? It sometimes occurs to me how little of me will be left in the world when I die. A few thousand preserved insects, a few essays no one will ever read. Not a lot is it?'

'Not a lot for what?'

'Not a lot to show, for a life.' He puffed out his cheeks and exhaled. He picked up the teacup again and drank quickly.

'Good tea this,' he said.

'It's a new blend. I'm trying it out. Want another one?'

'Well, as you're up,' he said and handed me the cup. I took it and checked it for traces of Placidyl left on the china. There were none. I turned to go back to the kitchen, then I stopped.

'Can I borrow your handkerchief?' I asked.

'My hankie?' he asked, frowning but already rifling in his pocket. 'Funny girl!' he said and he handed it to me. It was still folded, yolk yellow with polka dots.

After the second cup, I got him up out of the chair, groggy and staggering like a half frozen moth. He said,

'So tired' and then 'shall we go...' and that was it. He dropped on the cedar wood floor of the hall, heavy and slaughterhouse-warm like fresh meat. So with my hands in his armpits, I dragged him outside and his long legs bumped down the steps and when a couple walked by I propped him up and scolded him loudly for being so drunk.

I don't know if he was breathing when I folded him as neatly as you can fold a man twice your weight under the hood of the Beetle he bought for me. Out of a bottle I had taken from his study, I poured a little chloroform into his cheery, spotty handkerchief and pressed it gently against his nose and mouth. Then I dropped the hood of the Beetle and I locked it. As the afternoon cooled I drove that car upstate to a flooded stone quarry where the summer before Leo and I did field studies out in the woods. As I recall, he brought a picnic.

Anyway, back out of the woods and there's a track slopes right down to the quarry edge. I got out of the car, let off the parking brake and gravity did the rest. Truth is, I don't know what killed Leo, whether it was the Placidyl, the water, the impact or the car fumes from the hour long drive upstate. I don't know if he woke, like that moth, and felt the fear of what was coming or the loss of what was not. But for him, that night I was the pin.

Of course people came looking for him and when they asked, I said he was on sabbatical in Belize or Brazil or Brunei researching new species. Time passed and people stopped asking, but somehow I never stopped waiting for the news report of a car pulled out from those opaque quarry waters, a body discovered, for the hard rap of a cop at the door.

Someone said to me once, or maybe I heard it on the radio, that you're not a criminal until you get caught. Innocent until proven guilty and all that bullshit. Trust me, it's not like that. Your sentence starts right away, as soon as you've done it. As soon as the exhilaration or the relief or whatever it is wears off, it's there. For the rest of your life. Heavy. Like the mercury at the bottom of the thermometer, just waiting to rise up.

And that's how I took it, when that retribution yellow Beetle showed up this morning. This was the knock at the door I'd dreaded, this the hand on my shoulder, the sign. *Time's up*. This was the entomologist's pin.

So here I am, for a second time sitting in the Beetle at the top of the track down to the quarry near the woods. I arrived here a little before sunset. *Nice evening for it,* is what Leo would have said, all still vanilla-pink clouds spellbound on violet skies. An early moon's up but it's waning.

My hands feel the places on the wheel where Leo handled it smooth. I smell him again, a musty mix of old books, cologne and dry skin stirs memories, defrosting like moths. I feel him. I want to cry. That is, I feel like I should be crying. But I'm not.

I take off my glasses and put them in the glove compartment. I let off the parking brake and the car starts to roll. The window's open. Damp air rushes in, smells of coming rain and wood smoke. There's still time to change my mind. And then there isn't.

Make it quick.

They say, don't they, that in moments of trauma you see yourself from the outside? Like it's a film. Right now, I see a yellow car bouncing too fast over the track, then leaving the cliff edge and doom-swooping out into the smooth evening air, high over the water, with a delicate, lilac tail of exhaust. Madagascan Moon Moth. It's real quiet and look, there I am! A fleck of pale behind a wheel, telling it all, feeling it all. All the excitement, all the fear, all the regret and the release, all the pain, all the elation, all the

T.C. SMITH

A Woman of Paris (1921)

Jolene Franklin from Tyler, Texas, who now went by the name Cynthia, crashed the late afternoon party in Beverly Hills because she heard from the delivery boy at the corner laundry (a liquor front courtesy of Prohibition) that Charlie Chaplin was going to be there. ('Really? Really!!!' she screamed when she heard it.) Dressed in her only black, her only silk dress worth mentioning, she took the Red Line from Hollywood, poufing out her hair in a French tease as she rode. The sight of the opulent homes in the tony blocks past La Brea brought on some last minute soul-searching. She decided, if she caught his attention, she would let him kiss her (chastely) on the lips and fondle her breasts (above the dress), and that she might be induced to play in the pool in her skimpies, but if more were required, she'd flat out, but with respect, tell him to see her agent.

From the bus stop at Benedict Canyon, she walked back up Sunset and climbed the hill on Crescent to the address the delivery boy had charged a dollar and a ten-second kiss for. The dirt and scrub hills were already brown after the spring rains, but the mansions, hidden from gawkers and fans behind high walls, allowed a lushy green of hibiscus and palms to peek out. At the street entrance to 904 Cynthia ducked behind a dusty photinia and waited for a limousine full of pre-party drunks to pass in. A boisterous group came along right away. As the limo pulled up the short drive, she raced to the columned portico, hidden on the chauffeur's side, crouched between the car and an immense stone fountain. She then casually opened the rear door, scootched across the back seat, and out the other side, helped to her feet by an out-of-work actor dressed as a seventeenth-century footman.

'Hey, Cynthia,' the footman whispered as she passed. 'How do you know Fairbanks? I'm impressed.'

'Sorry?' Cynthia said.

'It's Nebraska Jerry from Edendale. We met last year on that Mabel Normand pic at Goldwyn.'

Cynthia smiled vaguely and walked on.

'Oh, I see how it is,' he called after her, then spit in the potted azalea behind one of the columns. 'You come with a star, he keeps you on a tight leash.'

Cynthia stopped. Jolene from Tyler blushed deep red and turned back. He was cute in a hick sort of way, sincere, and probably doing everything he could to get a part, any part, in someone's next picture. Definitely not date material.

'Jerry, if you do understand, don't spoil it for me,' she pleaded with a full-blown Texas accent, layered thick for Jerry's benefit. 'I didn't come with anyone. I just snuck in one door and out the other when no one was looking.'

Jerry's sour sneer turned to a smile.

'You're looking hot, very Louise Fazenda right now. So, you don't know Fairbanks then?'

'I didn't even see his back.'

'OK, party-crasher. Meet me for coffee next week and I won't turn you in.'

Cynthia poufed out her hair, flirty, the same way Fazenda had done in *My Goodness*.

'You know I'm not falling in love with you, Jerry.'

'And why is that?'

'Are you a producer?

'No.'

'How about a director?'

'Nope.'

'Perhaps you're a star of the silver screen?'

'Not yet.'

'What about a patron of the arts?'

'Still no.'

'Well then, Sugar, how could I possibly fall for you?'

'Have coffee with me and see. Monday at Schwab's, 10:30, a., not p.m.' And he turned back to the driveway to open the next limo door.

'I'm not looking for a man, Jerry. Keep it in mind.'

The interior of the house was vaguely Moroccan in that easy way Southern California had of appropriating a bastardized version of any and every architectural style or period. The only real features in the front room were an open tile fireplace in one corner and rows of beams that ran the length of the ceiling, rich and dark like the freshly plowed cotton fields of Smith County. In the far corner on a lumpy-looking horsehair sofa, sat Sessue Hayakawa and his wife, formal, aloof, imposing, alone. Nearby, half-hidden in an alcove behind the fireplace stood Oliver Hardy, Harold Lloyd, and Bebe Daniels, drinking. They laughed and swigged, and when Lloyd choked on an *hors d'oeuvre*, Cynthia was startled to see Hardy and Daniels hit him on the back, the same way regular folks did.

A man stepped up behind her and blew a stream of cigarette smoke over her shoulder.

'You know, beams bring a house luck,' he said in a clipped, tenor voice.

He sounded like a nervous accountant, Cynthia mused, an Easterner with no obvious social skills. Without turning round, she ranked him below third cousin to a minor star, a part-timer waiting for his big break as a stuntman, or an assistant to an assistant, or perhaps even as the office boy who licks the stamps. Which meant, if she were lucky, he might also be a producer. Cynthia crossed her arms under her breasts to give them lift. By the fireplace, a jowly man in a cowboy hat stared with narrowed eyes over the top of his drink.

'Is that good or bad luck? You didn't say,' Cynthia played along.

'Well, if they radiate out from a center, that's brings good fortune. Luck likes to spin its wheels, so to say.' He spoke fast, a little out of breath. More smoke poured over her shoulder.

'But these are parallel. That can't be good.'

'Right you are. Gloria is playing with fire. I doubt even her devotion to vegetarianism will save her.' Cynthia's ears rang. Everything he said ended in an exclamation point.

She scanned the room, looking for an escape. By the door, another man, this one an imposing, big-featured, boxer-type with a heavy brow, a strong chin, and a cauliflower ear, stared warily back at her.

'Gloria?' she said without conviction.

'Yes, our hostess, Gloria Swanson. Surely you know her.'

'Yes, of course,' Cynthia said and turned to face him, ready to give him the brush off.

Cynthia ran her eyes over his firm body, barely hidden by a tight-fitting dinner jacket, appraised his extremely wide shoulders (foundations of barns weren't that sturdy), then innocently lifted her gaze to meet him head on. His smile showed more teeth than an angry Chihuahua. Though he had charm, his piercing, predatory glare undercut the effect. He stood barely an inch taller than her, deeply wrinkled from either too much sun (he was burnt brown like a piece of well-done toast) or too much living. His chin was on the verge of doubling; his hair noticeably long and girlish.

'I know, the hair, right?' he said. 'It's for my next picture. That or a wig. I'm Douglas Fairbanks, by the way. I hear you came to the party in my car.'

And then she recognized him, 'The King of Hollywood'. The moment turned incendiary. The skin of her face grew hot, scorched by his charisma. The scope of her vision irised-in until only a point of light remained, her glance rolled its way upward, past his smile, his nose, his eyes, his forehead. Briefly, she saw the ceiling, but then her sight failed. So this is how one swoons, she thought, and was gone.

Fairbanks grabbed her around the waist. The men who had been staring raced to help.

'Have you eaten?' He said as he patted her cheek. He turned to his henchmen. 'Tom, Bull, help me get her to the bar.'

* * *

At Fairbank's raised finger, the bartender automatically placed a large glass of champagne on the zinc countertop in front of Cynthia.

'You should eat something,' Fairbanks said, and pushed the ebony bowl of peanuts towards her.

'Too fattening,' Cynthia replied. She picked up her glass and swallowed half the champagne in one gulp. Through the garden window on her right, the sun glinted, bright off the swimming pool like flashbulbs at a premier. Too bright. She leaned her forehead against the cool metal bar. Fairbanks ordered an orange juice. Behind him, the men who'd help escort her to the counter faded into the background. Cynthia sat up and focused on Fairbanks. Full of nervous energy, he shifted from one foot to the other. His stare said he was going to be trouble. She burped.

From the bar, Fairbanks grabbed a glass swizzle stick.

'Stir your drink with this. Dislodges all the bubbles.'

'But where's Miss Pickford this evening?' she said with studied calm.

'Mary? Oh yes, dear Mary has a migraine tonight.' As he spoke he grabbed a fistful of nuts and tossed them artfully in the air one by one, catching each in his open mouth.

'Oh, I'm sorry to hear it.'

'Don't be. That's just our way of saying she's home with her brother, Jack. He's Mary's baby. I bet you saw him in Tom Sawyer. All-American kid. All the Pickfords are great at playing kids.' The nuts now gone, he lit a cigarette. 'Only Jack's had trouble regulating his, um, medication since his wife died.' He rolled his eyes at Cynthia. 'Say, have you seen this one?'

Fairbanks stubbed out his cigarette and pulled a peacock blue handkerchief from his breast pocket. Not paying her any attention, he stumbled into a magic trick like an overly exuberant schoolboy.

Cynthia sighed and turned to the window. Guests, though no one famous, could be seen cavorting poolside. She leaned her back against the bar and rubbed her temple. Fairbanks's pictures never had more than one *ingénue* each. And rumor had it, casting lay in his wife's hands. Should she ditch him? But what if Chaplin never showed? A chance encounter could become a contact if handled right. Yes, he was boring, but that's what champagne was for. She picked up a fresh glass from the bar and drank deeply.

Fairbanks gave up on his trick and glared at her.

'I see you've found something more interesting than me,' Fairbanks said petulantly, and took the near-empty glass from her. He licked the swizzle stick, then stuck it in his mouth.

'Oh, I thought you were practicing,' she said. 'Surely, Mary wouldn't want you flirting, Mr. Fairbanks.' She scanned the crowd for Chaplin. 'We should talk about something neutral. Tell me about one of your co-stars. Adolphe Menjou. I know you know him. He was in your last picture.'

'No, that was Bill Lowery. If you want to know about Adolphe, talk to Adolphe.'

'What interests you then? The late war? The latest dance craze? Sports autos?'

'Lesson one: when you're with an actor, the subject is him. Otherwise, it's an act of war.'

He set Cynthia's glass down on the bar and shoved his handkerchief back in his pocket.

Embarrassed, she shrank into herself. Should she slink off into a corner? Probably. Would he remember her later and do her career damage? No need to answer.

'Look,' and she swung her head slowly back and forth. 'Do you see it?'

'See what?'

'The corn growing out my ears, all green,' and she smiled.

Fairbanks attention returned and he chuckled graciously.

'All right, two strikes isn't an out. Apology accepted.'

'You know, I really liked you in *The Half Breed*,' she said. 'Does that help? When are you going to make another picture like that?'

'My only flop. You're really striking out, kid. Maybe you should go back to Kansas,' he said, and he began to fence with her using the swizzle stick as a rapier.

'Texas,' Cynthia corrected him.

'Well, Tex, lesson two: the best way to insult an actor is to ignore his last picture. In my case, *The Nut*, with Mr. Lowery, which you've already so artfully referred to. You've seen it. I know you've seen it. You know that I know you've seen it. And now that you know that I know, I'll have you know it's been a pleasure.' He stabbed her in the heart with the swizzle stick, then turned to go.

'I am a clod, aren't I?' she said. 'I'm sorry,' and she reached out and touched his arm.

Without losing a beat, he turned back and laid one of his hands over hers.

'Now that's better.' He raised her fingers to his lips and kissed them. Then pulled her close. 'Not to worry,' he whispered in her ear, 'I'm a one woman man.' The sweet, acrid smell of cigarettes and cologne, the same aftershave her father used, engulfed her.

Cynthia put one hand on his chest and pushed gently back. 'But can you trust me?'

As she'd seen in the movies, she shyly lowered her eyes, then turned to face the window. Either he would pursue or apologize. She waited to see which. By the pool, two women in brassieres and panties were tossing a small leather-paneled ball back and forth. As she followed the up and back of the game, her Champagne-induced lightheadedness grew. Slightly dizzy, she stood in alluring profile, smiling at nothing at all. Let him find his own meaning there.

'Oh, so it's water sports you're interested in,' Fairbanks said. 'Why didn't you say so,' and he led her to the open patio doors.

'I've always wanted to sail around the world. Nothing between me and the sea. Not even a tan line.' He pointed to the redhead with the beach ball. 'Is that what you like? Not uncommon, though she's not much of a swordsman, I should think. Or do your tastes run more to the traditional?' and he pointed with the swizzle stick to a man sitting on the end of the lower diving board.

Cynthia squinted in the man's direction. Slowly it dawned on her that he was naked. Only once before had she seen a man stripped-bare—at the lake, her brother's college roommate, and only from the rear. But this view expanded her horizons by including a penis, not just on display, but one at full salute. She drew back, pale and shy, a little dazed from the surprise. From the bar, she lifted another glass, then while pretending to drink, she discreetly looked back at the man over the rim. Is that really what all the fuss was about? Somehow she'd gotten the impression of ramming pistons and out-of-control fuselages, whatever they were. She regained her composure and, forgetting her glass, stared openly at the all-too-human deity. How hard could it be to tame something that small? Like so many disappointing things, she decided, it all came down to vanity.

'Forgive me,' Fairbanks said huskily. 'I didn't realize. I don't go for men showing off their goods like that. Don't get me wrong, I'm all for public nudity, single-sex of course. Men naked with other men is healthy. But that, that's too public.'

Cynthia laughed.

'Pubic? Did you say?' and she laughed. 'But it's so silly, so exposed.'

Fairbanks's eyes widened. He wrapped one arm around her upper chest and pressed himself into her back. Through his jacket, she felt his muscles tighten.

'Ri-dic-ulous,' he whispered in her ear. 'The first one always is. But that's Kirkwood. Hard to imagine what Mary saw in him now the evidence is in front of me.' From the champagne bucket he dug an ice cube out with his free hand and ran it lightly along her bare arm.

'Are you flirting again?' she asked.

He dropped the ice and moved from arm to breast. Using the fleshy part of his palm, he massaged her nipple through the soft, light material of her dress.

'Can't you tell?'

'Then I think you'd better see my agent,' she said, and stepped away. Not sure she could look him in the face, she handed her glass to him, then cleared her throat several times while smoothing down the front of her dress with trembling hands.

'Oh? Is that so?' he said, placing the glass on the bar. 'And what might his name be?' With one hand in his pants pocket, he began to jiggle his loose change. He scanned the crowd for an escape.

'I can't say.'

He stopped jiggling.

'You *are* a tease. And why not?'

'Well, I don't have one,' and she blushed. 'Yet. But if *you* ask around, I'm sure somebody will bite and I'll have representation by noon the next day.'

A loud cheer went up in the front room, followed by the pop of a champagne bottle. The cries of 'Chaplin's here!' reached her long before he actually gained the bar. With him was a heavily veiled woman in a high-necked, black satin Paris gown. As she walked into the room, Chaplin's date bounced on her toes like an over-excited boy.

'Charles is here!' Fairbanks said. 'Finally, we'll have some fun.' He turned to Cynthia and covered his eyes like a toddler playing hide and seek. He peeked through his fingers with impish delight.

'Tell me, Tex, are you up for some mischief?'

* * *

Between the front of the house and the bar, the high-ceilinged dining room had been converted into a dance hall. Petite two-seat café tables lined both walls, with a bandstand set against the far row of narrow, curtainless Gothic windows. Cigarette smoke drifted through the room, like the dusty haze that perennially blocked the city's view of the mountains.

'Charles!' Fairbanks cried.

Chaplin looked up and squinted his eyes, taking aim.

'Doug!' he hollered back with equal volume. '*Amigo*!'

Immediately, the crowd parted, like a western town expecting a showdown.

'Is this your mother?' Fairbanks said. 'She's much too old to be your date. What, is she nineteen?'

'Oh, Doug, I didn't think you knew what sex was,' Chaplin returned fire, eying Cynthia. 'Where's Mary, your thirty-year-old perpetual child bride? Don't you have a wedding anniversary soon?'

'Monday. Let me introduce my niece, Nanette. Unlike most of the people here, she works for a living.'

'Something you might like to try on your next picture, Doug. And what do you do, my dear?'

'I'm a culinary aviatrix.'

'Next time you're in the air,' Fairbanks said, and he raised his little pinky high, 'she'll scramble your eggs for you.

Chaplin eyed Fairbank's hand on her hip. 'Let me introduce Trixie, my sister, visiting from Paris.'

Trixie offered her hand to Fairbanks. He briefly lifted it chin high, then released it without ceremony. Trixie flipped her fingers up and slapped him on the underside of his jaw.

'You haven't seen a lady before, have you?' she asked. The she laughed and patted him on his cheek. 'Or a razor.'

Cynthia tried hard not to laugh.

In the corner of the room, a small combo suddenly came to life and struck up their rendition of 'Whispering'. Fairbanks turned at the sound and lit another cigarette.

Cynthia offered up her hand to Trixie.

'It's nice to meet you,' she said.

Trixie automatically raised Cynthia's fingers to her lips. Chaplin slapped her wrist.

'Etienne!' he said. 'I mean, Trixie, you naughty, girl! Mother taught you better than that.'

'But surely, she's a man,' Cynthia blurted out.

Trixie and Chaplin exchanged worried glances.

Oblivious, Fairbanks watched the band and tapped his toes in time to the music.

Cynthia coughed. 'Surely she's a man killer?' she offered.

Chaplin's face relaxed. He stepped behind Trixie and motioned Cynthia with his eyes, rolling them with wild emphasis in Fairbanks's direction. Cynthia turned to Fairbanks, then glanced sidelong back at Chaplin, not understanding what he wanted her to do.

'I just love Paul Whiteman,' Trixie shouted over the music. She turned to Fairbanks. 'I just love to *dance* to his tunes,' she said, and held up her arms, waiting for him to follow her cue.

'Go on, Doug,' Chaplin said, 'she's slim-hipped like a boy, just what you like. Miss Niece won't mind? Chantel, wasn't it?'

Cynthia pursed her lips tight so she wouldn't laugh and spoil everything.

'What was that, dear?' Chaplin pursued.

'But of course,' she said, affecting a fake Swedish accent.

Fairbanks stood disconcerted.

'It's all right, Mr. Fairbanks,' Cynthia leaned over and whispered.

'I say, I'm not sure it is,' he whispered back. 'Just remember you're on my side,' then, with a European flourish, bowed his head in submission, took Trixie by the hand and stepped into her embrace. On the next upbeat, they two-stepped away in a lively, modified Foxtrot.

'Don't worry about Doug,' Chaplin said, 'He's got built in protection.'

'And what's that?' Cynthia asked.

'He's got no imagination. He thinks all of this is real. He throws himself into the void with abandon. Which is why he's a star and why we're such pals.'

'Opposites, you mean?'

'Oh, not just opposites. I also pull the strings. Like now.'

Chaplin looked after them, laughing into the back of his hand.

'I know you've already guessed?' he asked Cynthia. 'I dare say Doug will soon.' And he laughed a little larger without trying to hide it.

Cynthia looked at the dancing couple.

Fairbanks was growing more and more athletic. He hollered to her from the floor. 'Look at me, I'm dancing!'

'Dancing? Oh, Mr. Fairbanks, what you're doing is much better than dancing.'

Fairbanks did a double take, then let shine his toothy smile. He spun Trixie around and the two Foxtrotted to the far reaches of the room.

'But why the drag act?' Cynthia asked Chaplin.

'You'll see.'

Suddenly, another man, even shorter than Chaplin, slid his arm around her back from the other side. The two men both sidled up to her until all three were inseparable at the hip. As she was tallest, they leaned behind her and spoke, hidden by Cynthia's French-frizzed coif. They're all just little pixies, she thought.

'No time to lose, Max,' Chaplin said. 'Fairbanks will figure it out any minute. Nadine, keep a look out.'

'*Jawohl!*' Cynthia said with a low, guttural German accent. Both men pulled back in surprise.

Well, done *ma chérie*,' Chaplin said. 'If comedy weren't silent, I might use you. But back to business,'

He and Max disappeared once more behind her hair. Cynthia tried not to listen, but their lips were closer to her ears than her dangling, teardrop rhinestones.

'This almost makes up for it,' Max whispered.

'Stop blaming me,' Chaplin replied. 'I had nothing to do with releasing *Kid* the same day as your *Seven Years*. Ask First National.'

'But you didn't stop them.'

'No, I didn't. On the other hand I've told you and the press a dozen times what genius your mirror scene is.'

'But only you saw it. The theater was empty.'

'Well, there are no do-overs in Hollywood, my friend.'

'So, instead we act like asses at Mr. Fairbank's expense, to create the famous Hollywood publicity stunt. Are you sure the press will, what do you say? Run with it?'

'You'll be the talk of the town.'

Cynthia leaned back into the line of their conversation.

'Dancing pair coming in for a landing,' she announced.

The two men dropped their hold on her waist.

'No, no, no!' Max said. 'It's too soon.'

Chaplin took Cynthia by the hand. 'Once around the park, my dear?'

'*Mes oui*,' she answered in a fluty French accent.'

To Max, Chaplin added, 'Don't dawdle!' And he and Cynthia slunk into a tango at a gallop.

'Race you to the fireplace and back. Doug!' Chaplin called. Trixie followed their lead and swept Fairbanks across the floor. Waiters scrambled out of their way.

Max counted to ten, waited until the couples turned, then stepped into action.

He raced to the center of the room, grabbed Fairbanks with one hand, Trixie with the other, and wrenched the couple apart.

'So, you steal my girl!' he cried, then turned to the crowd. All dancing stopped, as did the music.

Trixie threw herself in front of Fairbanks.

'Don't touch him!' she cried.

'Tut, tut, my little tut-let!' Max replied as he dropped to his knees. 'There's only one thing I can say: Delicious Maiden, BE MY WIFE!'

Out of nowhere, a photographer appear. A flash went off and Max sprung immediately to his feet. 'Yes, ladies and gentlemen, my latest picture, *Be My Wife*, opens next Saturday. Be sure to see it!'

He took Trixie by the hand and the two bowed to moderate applause. Another picture was taken.

Fairbanks added his applause to the general surprise, then posing elbows out, fists on hips he bellowed his manly, movie star laugh.

'I would have milked it more,' Chaplin said to Max, 'but it's done. We're even.'

Cynthia stepped up to Fairbanks and put her arm through his.

'What a good sport, you are!' she said and kissed him on the cheek.

'How am I going to explain this to Mary?' he said.

Etienne bowed to Fairbanks. '*Monsieur*,' he said, then took Cynthia's hand in his and kissed it.

'Thank you for not giving me away.'

Fairbanks glared at Cynthia.

'What? You knew?'

'Only that she's a man.'

'What!' cried Fairbanks.

'After all, he did try to kiss my hand.'

'She's very quick on her feet,' Etienne added.

Chaplin hurriedly stepped in.

'Doug,' he said, 'meet my temporary assistant, Etienne Dussollier.'

Fairbanks turned to Trixie, then back to Chaplin.

'You mean he's not a she?'

'No, Doug, she's not.'

Fairbanks smile grew larger, the teeth sharper.

'Well, *Madame*,' he said to Etienne with stiffened posture, 'you dance quite well.'

'Oh Doug,' Chaplin jumped in, 'don't spoil Max's surprise. Here,' he hollered to the camera man, 'a picture of the lady unmasked.'

Etienne removed his wig and hat and looked sheepishly at the camera.

'Doug, why don't you join him?'

Etienne leaned over, bent his left leg up to show off his calf, and grabbed hold of one of Fairbanks's dinner jacket buttons. He smiled, then blushed in time for the flash. Fairbanks's button came off in his hand.

The combo started up again, though dancing did not.

What followed next was captured best by the Trades: 'Fairbanks gave a curt bow to Mr. Dussollier, and turned to go. As he spun on his heels, a waiter carrying a tray of *hors d'oeuvres* appeared. Fairbanks's elbow neatly upended the salver and sent little sausage rolls gleefully aloft, like startled pigeons or fresh, hot popcorn. The waiter swung the tray wildly in his attempt to catch as many of the greasy rolls possible. Unfortunately, in the confusion he stepped on Fairbank's foot and tripped. The waiter went down, the tray up. And as he fell, he grabbed at the stately Fairbanks's coat. The sleeve ripped away. The tray, meanwhile, arced gracefully towards the ceiling, only to come down hard on Mr. Dussollier's head. As he tottered from the blow, an unknown ingénue jumped forward. The two of them crashed into Fairbanks and all three upended in a heap.'

Another flashbulb exploded. The partygoers clapped enthusiastically.

The cameraman sprinted away. Fairbanks's men, Tom and Bull, gave chase.

'Out of work actress saves Chaplin's sister from Fairbanks's unwanted advances!' Chaplin called out. 'You are all witnesses!' And he burst into gleeful laughter.

'Great!' Fairbanks hollered from the floor. Cynthia and Etienne's eyes met and the party was over for them.

* * *

Later, while Etienne changed, Chaplin went off with Max to Musso & Frank, and Fairbanks and his men motored back to Pickfair. Cynthia sat on the front steps of the house waiting for Jerry to give her a ride.

So, she'd met Chaplin. And Fairbanks. And had a laugh, as well. But what had come of it? Not much. In the late afternoon light the fountain opposite the portico had turned a golden, silvery splash. As the sun went behind the hills, a waiter stepped out and flipped a switch below the spout. The waters stilled. It was time to go.

A petit Frenchman with a small suitcase walked up to her.

'Are you waiting for me, perhaps?' he said.

'I'm afraid I don't know anyone in the band,' she answered.

'But you don't recognize me? It is I, Trixie.' Etienne doffed his hat and gave her a small bow.

He laughed so charmingly, Cynthia joined in.

Etienne offered her his hand. As she took it, a spark ran between them. Cynthia giggled, then found herself blushing. The look in Etienne's eyes showed nothing but sadness. The warmth in her hand deepened.

'Thank you,' she said and leaned down to kiss him on the cheek.

'And what is this for?' he asked.

'For you, silly. I had a good time.'

Etienne smiled in thanks. Cynthia leaned closer and placed her hand on his chest.

'Please tell me you have a car,' she added.

'I'm afraid I don't. But we could walk to my place and see if we can borrow one?'

'Where do you live, a car park?'

'No, Charlie's guest house.'

'And I thought you were an out-of-work actor desperate for money.'

'But who isn't in Hollywood?'

Cynthia took his arm and put it through hers.

'Well, I'm game. Shall we?'

Etienne shifted his case to his outside hand and, with Cynthia on his arm, waddled down the driveway like the Little Tramp. Cynthia looked back towards the house. Nebraska Jerry waved from the shadows of the portico and shrugged his shoulders. Cynthia stopped and blew him a kiss.

At the street, Etienne waited. When she caught up with him, he doffed his hat in exaggerated greeting. Cynthia laughed. How could one man, this tiny, little man she didn't even know put every other man at the party to shame? And all we did was shake hands. He looked at her with expectation. A small boy, sad and trusting. There was no hurry, she thought. She took his hat and shoved it down on her head, and the two careened around the corner, hopping in sync on one foot.

GRETA STODDART

The Leavetaking

I was flying back from Malaga with a friend. We'd booked our tickets separately so were sitting a few aisles apart. I think we both liked this arrangement, although we didn't say it. We'd spent a fairly intense week together with her mother who had made certain demands on us. She had this great nameless need, and time spent with her – although she herself was often host – felt like a period of continual and necessary giving. And because no one, least of all the mother, could name this need my friend and I could never be sure if what we were giving was the right sort of giving, or if it was ever going to be enough. So we were feeling a bit drained, and relieved, I think, to assume the silence and anonymity that travelling alone can bring.

My seat was near the back, hers at the front. If I stretched up in my seat I could see the smooth brown helmet of her hair with the odd strand wavering in the sunlight that came in through the cabin window. I could tell she was reading from the way her head was bowed and still. And I knew what book she was reading because I'd shared a bed with her and on the first night, while she was brushing her teeth in the bathroom, I'd picked it up from where she'd placed it on the pillow and turned it over in my hands to see if I could feel what kind of book it was, and maybe, by extension, how or where she was in her life.

Because our seats were at opposite ends of the plane we disembarked via different exits. As I made my way down the steps at the back I looked towards the cockpit and saw that a tunnel had been attached through which the passengers at the front were being led to the Terminus Building.

The wind blew in my face as I walked across the tarmac. I could feel in the gusts a sharp rain. I pushed open a glass door and climbed two flights of stairs, dragging my case behind me.

I'll see her at the baggage carousel, I thought, then remembered we'd only brought hand luggage. I'll see her at Border Control, I thought, and when

I got there everyone had slowed to a long shuffling queue so there was a good chance I would. I looked along the queue as I approached it, in front and behind me as I joined it. I stood on tiptoe and craned my neck to look all around, but she wasn't there.

I'll see her at the Arrivals barrier, I thought, that'll be where she'll stop and wait. Or I'll stop and wait. Which I did but still she wasn't there. Maybe she's at the train station, maybe she's buying a ticket from the machine. Maybe I'll see her there.

And I began to realise that the further I walked away from the plane, and with it the last sighting of my friend, the lighter I felt. And as the possibility of not seeing her again grew so did the relief at being separated or, more particularly, at having managed to avoid, quite naturally, the ritual of separation I knew we'd feel bound to perform.

I'd always dreaded saying goodbye. It wasn't sadness at leaving the person so much as reluctance at having to enter the ritual. I wondered why it made me feel so uncomfortable. Was it because I felt forced to an awareness of the present while at the same time having to acknowledge both the past which I'd recently shared with that person and a future into which they were just about to disappear?

I thought about Malaga. There'd been a lot of talk.

That chapel, when was it built, who was that saint?

Oh, we must do this again – shall we come back in winter, what's it like in winter?

This need of yours (not that we spoke about it like that), *when did it start, and why?*

And I realised that we hadn't once spoken about what was happening to us at the moment of speaking, which made me feel suddenly as if all the time I'd been in Malaga I hadn't really been there at all.

So my friend and I parted. We simply walked away from each other without saying a word. There was no sense of loss or regret, we were just two people walking in different directions. And as we did time seemed to open up and grow wider and wider the further away from each other we moved.

I stood on the train platform, eager now to get away. I felt anxious. The last thing I wanted to do now was see her. Not because of any bad feeling I had towards her but because I didn't want to stop this silent radiating space we had created. It had attained a certain quality, like a spell, that I didn't want broken.

But, even then, a part of me thought I had to be seen to be still looking out for her (what if she were looking at me? what if all this was some sort of test of our friendship?) so I moved my head vaguely this way and that, making sure my eyes didn't settle, didn't actually see anything.

I stood like a stranger watching the train pull in. I took a seat in a far corner. A thin rain was spitting at the window. And as the train began to move – slowly at first, reluctantly – then gather speed and with it a sense of purpose, joy almost, my phone lit up.

I love you so much, it read.

I looked out of the window. The train was speeding past trees and houses and then a field in which a girl stood holding a woman's hand. She was waving wildly at the train with such a smile as if she really did love us all even though she couldn't possibly – with the speed we were going and all the reflection – have seen a single one of us. In fact the train might have been empty for all she cared.

HANNAH SUTHERLAND

The Arrival Fallacy

Harry is doubled over, cursin' at the photocopier, when I first see him. I'm walking towards him, soft, like a whisper. He's the new lad at work, the one who apparently did a crackin' interview and my boss just had to snap him up before another firm did.

He must have been more eloquent in interview form.

'Feck's sake, oh just *fuck off,*' Harry goes, giving the auld machine a boot with his polished patent shoes. The machine doesn't like this level of harming, and so it shuts itself down, like it's mocking him. It's saying *Ha ha ha Harry the prodigal new boy with your posh shoes and poor temper. I'll teach you some good manners and patience. Wanker.* I imagine the machine sticking its tongue out, which wouldn't be very practical, because, you know. Paper cut.

'Um,' I say, tapping his shoulder. 'Hello?'

'Woah, where did you come from?' he says, turning.

'When the photocopier comes back on, it's the red button you press, not the green one. It's all back to front.'

He gives me an expression which isn't dissimilar to the serial killer from last night's documentary I watched with Sinead.

'Oh. Yeah,' he says. We're the same height. We are exactly the same height. 'That is all back to front. How silly.'

Thank you so very much for helping me out, Emily.

Oh, you are so welcome, Harry. Welcome, welcome, welcome!

When the machine reboots, Harry succeeds in whatever important task he's doing, gives me a sharp nod, then heads off towards the exit. He throws his head to his hands, groans, turns around. 'Still getting my bearings,' he says, and heads in the right direction.

We speak four days later, this time about that riveting topic, curdled milk. I'm devouring a chocolate biscuit on one of the staffroom chairs, chatting away to Sinead. I'm trying to make the biscuit last because Ma's put me on this wild diet where I'm not meant to eat carbs or sugar or chocolate or anything fun for six weeks to lose exactly one stone, but I'm rebelling. Ma says it's meant to help *snag* me a man, which sounds almost painful. I reckon though if a man can't see past my belly, he's not a man I can be with since I'm a keen fan of eating. Ma laughs when I say this, like I am a Very Funny Individual, but I'm not even joking. Food over fucks, any day of the week.

Harry has absently poured milk into his coffee by the time I take my last chocolatey bite. He's on his way out the door when he makes a gagging noise, runs to the sink, slams down his mug on the counter and spits it all back up.

'Jaysus,' he goes. 'The fuck...'

'Ah, the milk's out of date,' I say. 'We were meant to throw that away. Oopsy.'

I walk over to him, peer in the cup at the floating specks of curdled milk, like croutons in soup, only less appealing. 'Yuck.'

He fills up a glass with water, downs it in one. I wonder if Harry regrets leaving his old job where the photocopier worked, and the milk wasn't revolting.

'This place,' he mutters under his breath.

'I'll make ye a new one,' I say. 'One with the good milk.'

He slumps on a chair across from Sinead who's ignoring him and scrolling through her phone, sucked in to this feckin' toxic comparison culture. Sinead's probably still fizzing that Bianca Geraghty got the promotion she went for last week. Bianca Geraghty plastered it all over social media before Sinead got the phone call to say she hadn't been successful. Sinead spent the night moping about how her life was over and how she'd forever be poor, living with me in our inner-city ghetto, instead of having the career progression she deserved. All incredibly dramatic of her.

'Bianca Geraghty even got a feckin' cake,' Sinead said, on the eve of the great disappointment. 'A congratulations cake in the shape of a pound sign.'

'Oh, how crass.'

'I wouldn't have got a cake even if I'd got the job. I never get cake,' she said.

'Ach sure, I'd have bought you one from Tesco,' I said.

'Well, that is something,' she said, very thoughtfully, like she'd come to a staggering conclusion about life itself. 'I'd have been totally fucked if you'd decided to make a cake yourself.'

In the staffroom, Sinead doesn't even look up when Harry thanks me for the fresh brew. I think he could be a nice man to get to know, underneath all this terrible angst.

A further eight days later, I'm pulling my arms through the sleeves of my new coat which is royal blue with a snazzy faux fur collar on it. I've saved up for this coat and I feel like the great Audrey Hepburn, if she'd have been a smurf.

'Emily, right?' Harry calls.

'Correct.'

'Nice coat,' he says. 'Very... bold.'

'Thanks! I'm fairly delighted with it myself.'

He's not wearing a coat, just his trousers which don't fit him properly and a brownish shirt, like paper that's been soaked in coffee to give an old-fashioned effect. It reminds me of primary school when we learned about the evacuees in World War Two. We'd get a piece of paper, stain it with coffee, wait for it to dry almost pissing ourselves with anticipation, and then write imaginary accounts on them. The whole classroom smelt strongly of coffee all week, but our wall display was cracking.

'Um,' he says. 'So, I wondered... would you like to go for a drink sometime?'

'Me?'

He frowns and looks at the linoleum flooring. 'It's just... I've newly moved to the city and I don't know anyone. I... it's fine. It doesn't matter.'

'Oh,' I say, feeling a sharp elastic band sensation ping against my lower belly. 'Yes. Lovely. I'd be *down* for that.'

I am so terribly uncool to be wearing such a lavish coat.

'Great. Grand,' he says, still frowning, but his mouth is in less of a line, there's more of a bend to it. 'Um, here's my card.'

He hands me it, printed on a fancy glossy rectangle. 'How formal.'

'It's for my number,' he says. 'It's at the bottom. And my email address.'

'I feel all important, getting your card.'

Sinead is waiting for me outside the building when we emerge. She'll be desperate for our nightly dissecting of office politics in the local pub, before going home to our tiny flat where we've forgotten to top up the metre yet again. It was obviously Sinead's turn, but she says it was mine.

'I shall bid you goodnight,' Harry says. He gives me a small bow, then off he pops.

'Weirdo,' Sinead says, and links my arm with hers.

I tuck his card into my purse and feel secretive and special, like I'm a wee girl again, digging for gold on the sandy hues. An endless sea of possibilities.

I'm over at Ma and Da's for the afternoon and Harry's texting. We've been texting loads, actually, over the weekend. He sends me memes and YouTube clips he thinks are funny, and some of them are. Like the one where the photocopiers are swearing at each other and the one where the boss slips on a banana peel, but some are mildly offensive, like the bimbo blonde being unable to open a bottle. I reply with laughing emojis all the same. I'm a brunette so.

'Ye surgically attached to the thing?' Da says, noting my phone. He's sitting at the table with me, sipping tea.

'Yes,' I say. 'It's my whole entire life.'

'What's his name then?' Ma says, folding the dishtowel, waiting for the toaster to *ping*. 'When do we get to meet him?'

'Och Ma,' I say, scowling like I'm fourteen again and she's caught me nicking money from her purse to buy a pair of heels from New Look. 'I'm only texting Sinead. There's no *man*.'

'Ye live with the bleedin' girl,' Da says, pushing his glasses up his beak. 'What more could ye possibly have to talk about?'

He shoots me a very proper look, like he's about to impart some excellent life knowledge but disappointingly he comes up with: 'About time ye started going for promotions.'

This chat again. Lucky me. What a grand way to spend my weekend. I'd have been better off in the baltic flat with Sinead, helping her fill out her application form for another promotion in another office. I don't want her to get that job and leave me, thus I'm here, listening to this shite.

'Never mind that,' Ma says. 'It's a man she's needing.'

Oh, here we go.

'Christ,' I say. 'Will I just pick up auld Jimmy Johnson off the street and ask if he'd like a good ridin'?'

Ma ignores me, pushes on. 'You'll be thirty next month.'

'Thanks for the excellent reminder,' I say, pulling the skin across my forehead, flattening it out. 'I'd somehow forgotten this milestone, pummelling ever closer towards my death.'

'Weesht, you,' Da says, flapping his hands in front of him. 'Less time spent with Sinead and more time dating nice men, that's what ye need. Or get onto any promotion! Just... do something. Anything.'

'I'm actually very content with my life,' I say, folding my arms as the toast leaps upwards, makes Ma jump.

'Nah, when you're married with kids, that's when you'll *really* be content,' Ma says.

She's cutting the crusts off Da's toast, hunched over, slicing them perfectly straight so not a single bit of toast is harmed in the separation.

Da doesn't even say thanks when she passes it to him, just takes it like it's what he's owed. Ma stands, bum against the counter, watching him, nibbling the unwanted crusts, goes, 'Aye. It's about time you settled down with a nice man, Emily. About time.'

I wonder, as Harry texts me about the massive sandwich he's just made with shite loads of filling, if he's this nice man I need. If he's arrived in my life, angry and awkward and a little bit strange, at the time when I'm required to finally settle down.

'Fuck that,' Sinead says, filling my glass with very red wine.

'Oh, I don't know,' I say. 'I think Harry's quite sweet.'

'All the lads at work rip the piss out of him,' she says. 'They think he's a right oddball, Em. And he's scowls all the feckin' time. You don't match each other personality wise, at all.'

'Opposites attract and all that and anyway, since when have I cared what any of the lads think, like, ever?'

The lads in our office are bunch of fuck bois who have a tally in gents' toilet with who they've fucked in the office. They enjoy ogling our arses and looking at our tits and going, 'Make us a coffee, love. Ta,' when we're not even making coffee.

'Nah, I don't think it's a bad thing that Harry's different,' I say.

'He's got murderer written all over him,' she says, which I think is highly unfair and quite extreme. 'But whatever. Do what ye want. If ye want to date Harry, date him. If you're happy being single, be single. If ye want to go for a promotion, go for it, but know that Bianca Geraghty might have an annoying wee sister who'll nab it from ye. Do what ye want. I don't think not having these things defines ye. Just be happy.'

I rest my head against her shoulder and wish she were a man because it would be easy to love her with all her greatness. She is a wise woman. The wisest! Everyone around Sinead is like a rotten apple, the kind I'd get in my packed lunch box at school because Ma needed them eaten and she 'didn't buy fruit to be wasted.' Sinead is the freshest, most appealing apple you've ever seen; we're all dull in comparison to her.

'Do whatever ye like with Harry. But if he turns out to be a killer, don't say I didn't warn ye,' she says, and then we burst out laughing. How funny! Wee Harry really being a killer! Oh, how silly we are!

I agree to meet Harry for this drink at an upmarket cocktail bar which I suggest, in the hope that he'll be buying all the drinks cause I'm skint. It's strange because in work, he completely blanks me. If it weren't for our texts and memes as evidence of our conversations visibly there on my screen, I'd think I'd made up our whole communication. I wonder if it's because he's a shy man and talking to me with my excellent chat would make him all flustered. Or it might be that he's embarrassed to be seen with me in work, for unknown reasons, because I'm delightful.

Harry's there first and he's sitting at a table, scowling at the drink's menu. There must be nothing on there he fancies which is a bit sad, given how extensive it is.

He looks up when he sees me, goes, 'You're late,' and then passes me the menu to look at. Being a serial sampler of this menu due to my monthly visits here with Sinead – right after payday when we are wealthy women who drink fancy cocktails for twenty-four hours – I know exactly what I'm having.

'I recommend the Pink Lady,' I say boldly. 'It's crackin'.'

'Christ, no thanks,' he says. 'I hate gin. Gives me the runs.'

Even though this comment is a turn off, I'm still hopeful that he might be The One. I made that decision you see, after Ma and Da and all their pestering, that I'd like to try and woo Harry into thinking I'm The One for him too. Sure, there's nobody else and I've given up on Tinder since my last three disaster dates of sloppy sex, egotistical men and the unsolicited images of genitals which arrived on my phone during Sunday lunch with my family. Sure, wee Nanna Deidre would have died of shock on the spot at the sight of Percy's petite penis, had she caught a glance. At least I know Harry and know he's not going to be a complete stalker if this doesn't go well. Sort of.

I study him as he goes to the bar to order our drinks. He's gone for a very safe beer. He's wearing these jeans which don't fit him particularly well and his thighs are chunky, just like mine. He's got his t-shirt tucked in, and it's got a picture of Brad Pitt on it, from Fight Club and his belly hangs over his belt, just a little, like mine does when I'm bloated. He must be going for some sort of vintage vibe, but I don't think it's quite hitting the mark.

'Are you enjoying your new job then?' I ask as he comes back, carefully balancing my swilling pink concoction and his pint. Some of my drink escapes from my glass and spills onto his hand as he places it down.

'Sticky,' he says, grabbing a napkin. 'Um, no. Not so much, but it pays the bills so.'

'I'm sure the longer you're there, the easier it'll get and the more you'll like it,' I say, trying to be all perky, in case this is the type of girl he likes.

'I'm enduring it,' he simply says.

We sit for a long while in silence, curiously watching a couple argue at the table right in front of us. She's ripping into him because he sent flame emojis to this girl who her sister works with. It all sounds very turbulent, lots of stress.

'I've never understood why people place such emphasis on longevity,' Harry says, out of the blue. I peel my eyes away from the couple and look at him and his angry face. Sure, it's even angrier than the male from the warring couple. 'I mean, you just said the longer I'm in that job, the more I'll get used to it,' he says, sighing. 'But, I mean, look at them. They're... obviously not very happy people,' he says, motioning to the couple. The women's just thrown her Pink Lady in the man's face which makes me want to cry, given how delicious the Pink Lady tastes and how expensive it is. 'But still, they *endure* it. They put themselves through it, and for what?'

'Excellent make up sex?'

'Because people think longevity equals success,' he says. 'That you've got to stick in and suck it up when we really shouldn't. If we're not happy.'

I think Harry is much too deep for me as a human being.

I sip my drink, feeling the fizz go to my head.

'We're always seeking validation from outside ourselves,' he says.

I'm feel like I'm at a lecture rather than on a date. I find myself nodding along, agreeing, just to make him like me, because when he's all fired up like this and wise and preachy, he's endearing and attractive, almost. I place my hand on his knee and he doesn't flinch or move away, just keeps talking on and on and on, and so I peck him quickly on his cheek, to make him quieten.

'Oh,' he says, putting his fingers on the spot where my lips just were. 'That was unexpected.'

'Oh,' I repeat.

'It wasn't bad,' he says quickly. 'It was just... unexpected.'

'We could go back to yours,' I say, feeling the sharp jab of his kneecap underneath my palm. 'So we have more privacy.'

'But you've not finished your Pink Lady and it cost me eight pounds fifty and a quarter of it landed on my hand. At the very least you should dr...'

I pick it up, down it in one. 'There. Let's go.'

We wait for a while in the taxi rank, amongst the Young People. They're mostly very drunk with elastic limbs pulling on each other to balance themselves, pretending they can walk in a straight line, but when they obviously can't, they stumble downwards again, laughing ridiculously, like they're all just fucking hilarious, and this is the best night of their lives. I feel old. Very old. And boring. And when did this ageing happen to me? I quite fancy joining them, but I imagine they'd take one look at me and just *know* I am old, very old, and also boring.

I feel jealous of a girl with a pretty face who reminds me of Sinead and she's wearing a dress that makes both men and women stare at her tits. They are universally appreciated tits; everyone can enjoy them.

Not only is this girl winning at life in the genes pool, but she has a lovely man standing there, with his arm around her waist, kissing her neck and purring into her ear.

I move towards Harry, rub myself into his body, look at him with my eyes all wide and obvious, willing him to look at me in this way, but he shifts and goes, 'Um, you should wear a thicker coat next time. If you're cold. Although I do like this blue one.'

What a deeply romantic man. I'm swept clean of my feet.

He lives on the other side of town from me, in a small one-bedroom flat that appears immaculate.

'Take your shoes off,' he says.

I think about making a joke, about what a shite chat up line that is and how he should surely be ordering me to remove my bra, but he's looking very serious, as though I'll spoil his expensive cream carpet if I walk an inch further, and so I keep my jokes to myself. I'm at his actual flat, so I suppose he doesn't need chat up lines anymore. He's *snagged* me already.

I kick my ballet pumps off, hang up my lovely blue coat and wander around his living room for a while as he gets some wine from the kitchen. He's got lots of Lego on his shelves, and books and Mr T sitting next to a Dalek and Cyber Man with Yoda nestled in beside them, all staring back at me.

'Wine,' he says, emerging from the kitchen, passing me a glass. 'Cheers.'

'Cheers. I like your wee pals,' I say, cocking my head to Yoda. 'Feel the force!'

He laughs.

'Me too,' he says, and gives me the first smile he's ever given me, and Christ, I understand why he doesn't give these out regularly. Those teeth. That expression. Sure, he looks like he's snarling. Oh dear *lord*, he *is* away to murder me, right before my thirtieth, before I've accomplished all Ma and Da's plans for me. What a way to go, with those wee dudes, all staring at me and the last thing I'll ever see are those peggy teeth.

'Ma wants me to settle down,' I blurt out, as though mentioning her will stop him from the killing of Emily Dargie. *I have a family you know,*

I shout internally. *They may be disappointed by every life choice I make, but I still belong to them and they will miss me.*

'Oh, right,' he says, wrinkling his forehead.

'Yes. She thinks I will finally be content when I meet the right man.' Christ, why am I talking?

'I see,' he says. 'Parents, eh?'

'Yes. Parents,' I say.

He smiles again, but it's a better smile, and he motions for us to the sofa, and we sit there together, just smiling. Ach, he doesn't look much like a killer now. He just looks like harmless Harry from work who I may or may not have a wee crush on.

It might be the wine and the downing of the Pink Lady, and the feeling of floating, of belonging to the air, that when he turns to me and looks directly into my eyes in a way that nobody has looked at me before, I feel special. He leans towards me and clinks his sharp teeth off mine. It sends such a shock through the front of my entire face, that I've to fight the urge to laugh, or perhaps cry. He gets to chewing on my lips. I think it's quite nice at the start, that it means he's extremely attracted to me because he wants to eat me, but then the mauling of my lips continues and I'm very aware that he's biting them. Sticking his sharp incisors into my flesh and nibbling like its food.

'Ouch,' I say, pulling away, when I can bear the pain no longer.

I'm not sure I want Harry to be my soul mate anymore. Don't know if I can hack having my lips mauled so ferociously for the rest of my life. I'm quite fond of my lips. Would be a terrible loss to lose them.

'Sorry,' he says. 'No biting?'

'No biting.'

We start again and it's better. Not perfect by a very long shot, but more acceptable.

I open my eyes while we're kissing and see that he's got his eyes closed but his forehead is crumpled, and I can't tell if he's enjoying himself or not. He's flushed. He's getting into it, his body's moving in an up-and-down motion already, grinding the air. I wonder who he's picturing in his mind. I close my eyes and try to picture a fine Taron Egerton in front of me. Now I'm getting into it too. I straddle him on the sofa, kissing and sucking and rubbing, with Taron's face at the forefront of my mind. I feel his modest cock pressing against the band of his trousers that I can't help but brush as I stroke his body.

'Urghhhhh,' he lets out a loud guttural groan and flops his head onto my shoulder. 'Oh, *god*. Fuck. *Fuck.*'

Oh wow. What just happened?

'Harry?'

He carefully picks me up, like a doll, and puts me on the sofa, squeezes his eyes shut, goes, 'Um. Oh, fuck.'

'It's fine,' I say. 'Look it's just completely fine. I'm a very nice girl. I don't mind at all...'

'Christ. I'm so embarrassed,' he goes, and he scoots away up the stairs, head down, boxers full, semen undoubtably soaking their cotton. I wait for a few moments until the door closes, then bury my head into the sofa, pulling a cushion over it. God, I want to *die*. I could just *die*.

I wonder if I should leave. 'OMG get out,' Sinead replies when I text her. 'Run,' then 'If ur not home by 11 I'm calling the polis.' But I don't think I should leave, on the account that we work together. I'm patient. I wait.

'Hi,' he says, in different trousers. 'I wasn't sure if you'd be gone...'

'I really didn't mind,' I say, smiling. 'Honestly. I was very much into it too.'

He reddens and looks at the carpet, which really is a lovely plush material and I totally get why he didn't want shoes on it, but I wish he'd look at me, so he'd know everything was okay.

'I'll walk you to the taxi rank, Emily.'

This... this is the most disappointing part of the evening.

We walk with a distance between us, me near the pavement, him at the side nearest the houses. I wonder how work will be with him the following week, but then I remember he doesn't talk to me there anyway and so it will be exactly the same, only I'll have seen him in a very vulnerable state.

I feel his business card in my purse as I make sure I've cash for the ride home, but the feeling of being special, the thrill of Harry and his possibilities, has gone. Instead of finding treasure in the sand, all I'd get were empty shells and pointless rocks, just to be tossed back into the sea. It was always disappointing, finally getting what I wanted to realise the dream of it was better all along.

Perhaps I'm not bound for life's great arrival, where everything will be perfect and wonderful, and I'll live happily ever after with a man who adores every hair on my body, even those pesky ones around my bikini line which grow at an alarming rate, far quicker than the hair on my legs, probably just as quick as those few random strands underneath my belly button. Perhaps–

'Look out!' Harry calls, but he is too late.

As if in slow motion, a car approaches, tunes banging. The darkened window rolls down and a gloopy, pink substance is launched in our direction. It is like being shot by unicorns. An explosion of brightness. And it's sticky, and smells of milk, and it's bleedin' everywhere.

'Ha ha ha,' voices from the car go, speeding away. 'Feckin' losers.'

'Are you okay? Oh *god,* are you alright?' Harry asks. 'Was that... milkshake?'

My coat. My beautiful blue coat. My coat is ruined, and Harry came in his pants and I will never meet my soul mate because he probably doesn't exist and now, I am crying, in the middle of the street, covered in bleedin' strawberry milkshake, and if this wasn't so upsetting for me, I'd definitely laugh at the hopelessness of it all.

'Let's go,' Harry says firmly, holding my hand, pulling me back towards his.

He's going to murder me anyway. Sure, may as well die. This coat is discontinued.

'It's okay,' he says, forcing me to walk towards his den for the killing. 'Please don't be upset.'

He takes my coat from me as soon as we get to his home, starts sponging it, his forehead crinkled.

Maybe Harry kills me in an hour. Maybe he doesn't.

'Um. They got your dress too. Just go upstairs and help yourself to some of my clothes,' he says. 'I'm not precious about my loungewear. Just whatever you can find.'

Maybe Sinead finds my body tomorrow, stuffed in plastic bags, dumped ungraciously by the harbour. Maybe she doesn't.

In his bedroom, I look under his pillow, his bedframe, in the chest of drawers and cupboard for clues – knives, a gun, cable. Anything untoward. There's a photograph of him, scowling, and a similar-looking older lady who is scowling too. This gives me comfort, that he was just born with that raging face, the way I was born with a mole above my crotch that I catch every time I shave. I never learn. It bleeds terribly.

When I'm changed, I sit on the sofa, all curled up, with his wee pals watching us.

'That's the best I can do with your coat. It's still lovely,' he says, then shakes his head. 'Those arseholes.'

'Very kind of you.'

Maybe I need to just live right now, in the moment, with feckin' Yoda and Harry and his wonky teeth and crumpled frown and be present.

He gives me a small smile, strokes my cheek with the back of his hand. 'Tonight was a feckin' disaster, eh?'

I let out an actual snort and his shoulders shake and then we're both laughing our absolute holes off.

KATHY TIERNEY

The Hot House

Definition

1. Botany: a greenhouse in which the temperature is maintained at a fixed
   level above that of the surroundings.
2. An environment that encourages rapid development.
3. An environment where there is great pressure.

(Collins English Dictionary)

The Hot House
Lucy

When I think of Victoria, I think of a wooden mannequin, or what men call a real woman: tits pulled out of place, perked up in a bra: *Vintage, deadstock 1970s Maidenform Tric-o-lastic, size 32C, Marilyn Monroe style, nude color.* Look at the frigging names in that bra: *Vintage, deadstock, Maidenform, Marilyn Monroe, nude.* I would have called that bra,'how to kill yourself'.

The other way to kill yourself, is to live at 92 Fifth Street in the rustic outskirts of Melbourne, in a house that went brown like everything else in the 1970s; every room, except for the kitchen, in dark wood panelling, burnt orange carpet and brown upholstered furniture. And a sister, brown as tradition as well. Victoria.

I feel slobby next to her. But my sister and I are made of different textures. I'm stuck in the rough draft of a poem, I'm all crossed out, scribbled over, scrawled on. I can't get to the next draft. I wouldn't want to. Neatness scares me. Victoria. She is trying to take me out of the rough draft of woman.

'Victoria. There's a man at the back door asking to see you,' our mother called out from the kitchen.

Victoria looked up from her folder of neatly cut and clipped recipes. *Yuk,* I thought, staring at them, *Creamed Eggs in Corned Beef Crust, Lamb Kidneys with Rosemary, Seafood Loaf, Cheese Balls.* I knew when Victoria started studying recipes like that each day, it meant she was in pander to the latest stiff she was dating. Victoria could make a man's stomach orgasm like a dick. But using 1920s tit mannequin methods to get and keep a ring on. *Fuck.* She had a weird type of amnesia when it came

148

to feminism. It was something quickly forgotten in her, as if only female type bloomers were worth remembering. There was just no bloody tiger there. Not once has she clawed a person's face off.

'Who is it, please?' Victoria asked.

Victoria speaks like her job; voice neat and careful, straight as the chalky white letters she writes on a blackboard. Or maybe she got her precise way of speaking from studying the Queen, as she often did, watching how she moved and spoke.

'I don't know who it is,' my mother said exasperated, turning around at the kitchen bench, the small knife she held to cut the onions, pointed at myself. Mum had quiet ways of saying things, I thought edgily, stepping backwards. I looked tetchily at the old white stove; water bubbling in the large silver pot. Nearby, on the laminated brown bench was a chopping board with cut up parsley, gruyere cheese and brown onions. A large slab of sourdough rye bread was on a plate, next to a dish of soft butter. *French Onion Soup again!*...I thought angrily; Mum's idea of exotic cooking. I avoided looking at the dark brown cupboards, they made me think of small funeral boxes, lined up in a row. *Kitchen of the Dead...*

My mother gave her another one of her sour looks. 'I can only offer you a general description called man.'

Mum, I was sure, was named after the coldest month. *June*. Come out of the womb, with a frigid face. It was at odds with her short puffy auburn hair, combed over her ears, as if she didn't want to hear anything. I didn't like her dark grey skirt, with spills of cream and honey flowers over it, either, or that white and blue kite patterned shirt she had on. She was like this one big *mismatch*.

A general description called Man. Generality, I thought scathingly, *another* female sin; like hiding your real curves under a huge blown out shapeless dress. I often asked myself; what does my mother *really* think? Because her answers were routine as the same slick of vegemite on toast each morning, no marmalade tang on the tongue. Just a quiet, broad spread of sourness.

I spun around and faced Victoria.

'Ooohhh, how long since your underpants have been near one of those?' I asked Victoria, looking at her plump white thighs firmly pressed together underneath her dark grey, knee length, Chanel Brown pencil slim skirt. Couldn't stand her hair either, a big dark bouf at the front, with a neat little curl in front of each ear, cut short at the back. She looked like a high-class elf, *just* couldn't stand it.

Victoria. She would grow her legs longer for a man. She's not a woman through her own eyes. She's a woman through a man's eyes. And at the back door a man is here for her. Holding a fat balloon of fairy tales. Stupid loveable bitch. She'll take one.

'Er…Victoria?'

We *all* heard the man at the back door then.

'He talks like a wasp is in his scrotum, Victoria,' I told her.

'Do you have to talk like that?' she asked, her eyes lowering, her head turning away. As if my face was off a riot poster.

'And do you have to talk like three bras are wrapped around your tongue? Take them off sister,' I demanded.

'Can you two stop it,' her mother asked tiredly.

'Well? Victoria belongs in the Dictionary of Grandmothers. Have you seen what she calls underpants? Her bum looks like a big fat bell in them.'

'Can you get the door, please Lucy?' Victoria asked stiffly.

'No, get it yourself,' I said irritated how she talked to me as if I was one of her eight-year-old students, she could order around, which told me, she thought of me as *smaller, lesser.*

Her lips tightened. Tight as Scrooge at Christmas time.

I tossed a flier down in front of her. Her eyes lowered to it, with the same carefulness as a curtsy.

'Women's Rights Rally. Starting at the General Post Office, Corner of Bourke Street and Elizabeth Street, Melbourne, October 28, 1972, 2.00 pm,' she read out. She raised her eyes, looking speculatively at me.

'And?'

'Well, I want you to go with me – '

'Lucy, can you *just* get the door?' her mother asked, her voice as if a musician was tightly tuning her larynx.

'No, *shan't.*'

'Fine,' Victoria said distantly, which she did when she was enraged. I so wanted to see her cheeks burn, her eyes red as Satan, but her mind was like a white lace handkerchief, that kept the snot out.

She rose from the table, smoothing down her skirt. She looked carefully at herself in the oval mirror, framed with iron lace. She patted her hair, looked at her soft pink lips as if ticking them, *just the right shade, just the right amount.* She nodded to herself approvingly.

Yes. I, me, Queen, I thought sarcastically, watching her. Victoria walked to the back door, as if walking on a ruler of centimetre's, each footstep exactly measured.

She really did belong in The Dark Ages of Woman, I thought in disgust.

Victoria

I made my way to the back door. My mother's radio crackled in the kitchen, buzzing through the flute music. *Maybe a storm on the way,* I thought. I glanced out the kitchen window. The sky looked like a pale blue half eggshell, with cracks of dark grey cloud. Lucy's strange clothing, haphazardly pegged on the A-frame clothesline, flapped in the wind. Some sleeves and pants had slipped out of the pegs and the ones that weren't dangling by one sleeve or trouser leg, were tangled in the thick wild bushes surrounding the clothesline. *Like Lucy,* she thought. *Bits of her in order, bits of her in tangle or disarray.*

I saw him by the door. I tried to repress my irritation at the bits of torn mesh on the screen door fluttering in the wind. My mother would not fix it as she did not wish to interfere with the flight path of bees, flies, and moths. *Flight should not be met with mesh.* It disturbs natural order, my mother had told me. And you must not disturb the natural order, or bees will not make honey.

I decided not to mention that moths may make larvae in the food if she let them have a natural flight path through holes in the mesh. And perhaps flies may drop their germs on the clean kitchen benches. And bees may sting us all on their way through. Lucy was often very bitter about our mother's deference and reverence for mere insects, and none for her.

'Yes? Can I help you?' I asked, looking carefully at the tall, thin man with spectacles and thin brown hair neatly combed to one side. He didn't appear to be a threat, not a man tidy as that. His brown eyes were patient as a priest, and just as solemn.

'My name is Thomas. I'm here on behalf of Gregory.'

Gregory.

'Yes,' I asked, my breath quickening.

'He…' Thomas looked down at his feet.

I had seen children in my class do this. I knew it was when they didn't want to say something.

'Please. Say what you have to say,' I said, bracing myself, my eyes sure and steady on his face.

'Gregory does not wish to date you anymore. I'm sorry. He's looking for some-one with…more spark.'

'Am I to understand, I am getting a Dear John letter at the door?'

He looked at her sympathetically. 'I'm sorry.'

Lucy

Victoria came back into the house, looking like a shadow just fucked her.

'What's the matter Vicks?' I asked.

She looked away from me and down to her left. Now she may regard me as a screwball sister, but when she does that look away and down to the left, I am with it enough to know it means she's hit the lowest note on the piano.

'Did you limit yourself to one man, and lose him Vicks?' I asked.

Victoria usually made it a policy to have one. Just one. That was her policy on everything. One Earl Grey Tea a day. One glass of white wine. One man every century. She may as well be hitting the same note on the piano all the time. *Look at all the F sharps, D minors, A flats she is missing. She's like one big Middle C, with crossed legs.*

Victoria's fingers stumbled over the flier on the table, picking it up. She turned to me.

'He thinks I'm boring.'

I looked down tactfully. 'I think as a woman you are in the wrong place,' I told her bluntly. 'There are other places outside granny fanny types, you know. The 1970s is not the wormhole of womanhood, where we disappear out of our bras and those disgusting big undies you wear. Try spreading your legs a little, you could do with an air out down there anyway, there's mothballs up your fanny.'

'Do you think you could talk more discreetly,' Victoria said.

'No,' I said.

Victoria sat down at the table, neatly placing the flier in front of her. She looked towards the back door, her cheeks flushing, her eyes finally losing that blind look. She looked down at the flier again, her breath coming faster.

'There are numbers above one, Vicks,' I advised, looking at the flier. 'Try them.'

Victoria

As much as I love my sister, I sometimes get irritated by her oscillation. The only thing steady about her is her fingers on the piano. But a man once said to her (and I've never forgotten it, because I spent all night wishing so much, that such words were said to me), he said; *'Lucy, you make everything around you look like winter.'*

Lucy

'Today is your baptism with Germaine Greer,' I told Victoria, placing my hands on her hair, 'The braless Goddess bless you, for this new day.'

'Lucy. Please. Take your hands off my hair. I only agreed to watch your riot. To see what apparently more interesting women do.'

'I think you are compromising yourself, Victoria, selling out on what makes you, you,' our mother told her.

'I'm not good enough,' Victoria said. I could see her holding onto her breath until her bottom lip stopped trembling.

'And this is another new day,' I said, throwing my arms up and spinning around the room, 'Victoria's lip has wobbled for the first time since she was two,' I spun to a stop and lowered my arms. 'You have to lose some of that fatness. It goes with what is honoured by Mr Testicles: *plump, timid, delicate*. The Feminine Normal! Praise the apron, praise be.'

'Really. You don't need to turn this day into a feminist prayer. I'm uneasy enough as it is.'

'Men are now uneasy with you, Vicks. Your Gregory has had a taste of the new woman and he wants more. Your poached eggs and lasagne bake and once a year dick stab in the fanny, *not enough*. And those *clothes...*' I said, looking her over. She wore an apricot A frame dress, hem just above the knees, and a light pink silk scarf, knotted loosely in a bow around her neck. Her feet rested in sandals of cream leather.

'*Jesus,*' I said.

'I'm not wearing that,' Victoria said, looking pointedly at my crumpled T-shirt, with a bright red logo which read *Divided we stand*.

'This is the stop era,' I snapped, 'and you are now in wax woman wear, an outfit that says you want to stay in the museum of woman.'

'I'm not wearing it,' Victoria insisted, 'it's cheap and inflammatory.'

Our mother looked up from the National Geographic magazine she was reading and frowned at me. I looked at the mag in disgust. *Another* thing from the mothballs era, an 1888 skeleton rattling its scientific and geographical bones *in this loungeroom*. Every morning, when I got up and walked out of my bedroom door into the loungeroom, I wanted to close my eyes again; the brown velvet L-shaped lounge, the disgusting braided round rug, in shades of dirt, clotted cream and tan, the white triangular fireplace; embedded with brown stones, and a puffing red hollow at the base, the light brown tiles in front of it, and to the left, a pile of neatly stacked logs in a steel basket. As if there wasn't enough friggin' puffing in the house.

'Please, Victoria,' said our mother, in that sour, yeasty voice of hers, 'don't go to that rally. *Don't* change who you are because a man doesn't want you.'

'I want to see what's so special about the new woman and why women like me must be put away in "the museum"'.

Our mother shook her head, her eyes returning to the page. 'You may not be able to return as you were, Victoria. That bra burning lot will wreck your thinking. Make you mad,' she turned a page over, 'it's just a fad, Victoria. It won't last. Most women in this country don't care about it anyway. Please don't change yourself so easily.'

'I'm not that easily convinced,' Victoria said, picking up a cream leather handbag that looked like a box on a chain. She placed it carefully over her shoulder.

'Show me what I'm missing,' she said to me.

Victoria

This is where I am supposed to cast off myself, let this mob of women revise me. Here in this old Melbourne street, where women, despite their demands for individuality, are all wearing the same T-shirt with the same message, screaming out the same slogan.

I pressed my back further into the brick wall of the Melbourne General Post Office, finding some sense of safety in it's solid classical character; a Renaissance design, just like me. It had been around a long time, since 1861; now three floors and a clock tower, sitting on the north-eastern corner of Bourke and Elizabeth intersection; a popular place for protests. I thought briefly about the anti-Vietnam war protestors in Bourke Street two years ago, 70 000 of them. This was war of a different kind. Women against men, or the idea men had of them. *What was so wrong with that idea? Man taking care of woman... not woman taking care of herself. And according to Gregory, I was expected to be more enthusiastic, more sparky, lose my solidness. The traditional man seemed to be phasing out...which left me where?*

I looked gingerly at the women massing, red T-shirts clinging damply to their bodies, sweat gleaming on their skin. Shop owners on both sides of Bourke Street shut their doors. I did not feel safe here, with the tall buildings on both sides of the street making me feel pressed in and lost with all the unpredictability a protest brought. A group of Police passed by. Should I follow them? Sit safely in the Police Station and wait until it was over?

'Whoo-hoo!' screamed a woman, splashing some water on a woman nearby, 'put out the fire in that mouth baby, cops nearby...'

'What's the fucking point in being here, if I have to shut-up,' she yelled.

I looked away. Loud kids in the playground I could handle, but loud women at a rally? There was no behavior management plan ... and I doubted one would work anyway in the age of Germaine Greer. I took a white lace edged-handkerchief out of my handbag, wiping the sweat from my upper lip away. I almost put the handkerchief over my nose; the air was heavy with heat, permeated by a stale industrial smell, after the recent rain.

I thought perhaps the best tactic was to not do anything, so I would not be noticed, just manage myself.

I looked warily at the marching group of women, completely filling Bourke Street, their bodies pressed thickly together, waving hand painted signs 'No Barbie Dolls!' A woman, chasing them to keep up, shoved a sign in my face that read 'End penile servitude!'

'AGREE?' she yelled at me.

I should close my eyes, *close my eyes*, but I've closed my eyes to it long enough, gone on the way I am, and the way I am, no one wants…

'DROP THE MOP!' she screamed at me.

'*Come on* Caroline,' yelled one of the mob in front of her, 'She's old school.'

'Yeah. Don't waste your time on her,' another yelled.

My face burned with humiliation. *I'm not seeing a new woman,* I thought, *I'm seeing an uncivil one.*

I gazed around the crowd for Lucy. She was right in front of a group of women, fist punching the air, dark glasses slipping down her nose. Her long red hair fell over her face as the group rushed forward.

I looked at them cautiously.

'Come on Vicks!' Lucy yelled out, 'get your ticket out of bloomers world!'

I shook my head. No. *No.*

Three women from her group broke away, making their way towards me.

'Come on Prissy. Lose your bloomers!' One of them yelled at me.

'No. No. I just came to watch,' I called out politely.

Please go away, I thought, as I watched them shove through the throbbing crowds of women.

One of them, a large woman with a black afro, pushed her sweaty body against mine.

'Welcome to the sisterhood!' she boomed.

I don't want this, I don't want this, I don't want this!

'No. Really. I'm quite happy as I am,' I said, struggling against her.

'If you were, you wouldn't be here sweetheart. You'd be panderin' away to your man. Shake your salt out sister, we want you bitter! We want you yelling, we want you a big screaming animal.'

Before I could stop her, she grabbed my arm, her strong fingers digging into my flesh. She had the grip of a man. I tried to pull away, but she gripped my arm even tighter. I did not know how to manage this aggressive woman who clearly wanted to dominate me.

'Please. Let go of my arm,' I said, trying to control my panic. 'I will find Police if you don't.'

She rushed forward through the crowd with me. Another woman grabbed the skirt of my dress, lifting it up a couple of times. 'We are sure the last century lives up there!' she said laughing.

'Lucy!' I screamed, as they pushed me through the crowd.

She turned her face searching for mine.

She put her hand up to the other women, shaking her head. 'No. No!'

I was hit by a rush of women, and as I fell to the ground, my head hitting the hard tar, blacking out, I saw myself at ten years old, my feet sinking down in the ocean bed, a large rolling wave, curling over me.

Lucy

What have I done? What have I done? Look at my Vicks, lying there like that, because she climbed out of her glass coffin. She looks so white, so stiff. Not that she moved much anyway, not in her brain, anyway.

Mum came in carrying a tray with hot soup, a large slab of sourdough bread, and a glass of water.

'French onion soup again?' I asked bitterly.

'Victoria likes it,' Mum told me, placing the tray down on the table next to Vick's horribly made bed. It was tucked in tighter than a facelift, *not* a wrinkle. I don't know how she friggin' slept.

'Well, what about what I like?'

'What you like, changes every day, and I could never keep up,' Mum said. 'I don't think *anyone* can keep up with you.'

'Dad could.'

'Well he was like you,' she said abruptly, 'Mad, but gifted.' Her mouth tightened. 'I'm going to see to the ironing. I've got twenty more baskets to do, before tomorrow,' she looked over at me, her face hard, 'perhaps it's time you lived in reality. That's where natural flight is. Look where all this fiction about women got you. Your sister could have *died*.'

Not going to answer.

I looked out the window, at the faded green paddock nearby. A bull was wandering around it and a few dumb cows. I didn't like them; had wide staring eyes, like they just didn't get it. I heard a low grumble of thunder and squinted at the sky. Dark clouds hung down like thin drips. A thin fork of lightning glimmered.

156

'Wake her up and feed her,' my mother said, leaving the room. I looked at her, so pissed off. Vicks could still feed herself. She had been knocked out, but in my opinion, she was knocked out anyway. Germaine Greer was also busy knocking Sleeping Beauty out of women, but some of them didn't like that. Wanted to stay exactly as they were, in the wax museum of female horrors. But Vicks...I felt so bad. Smashed up by my group of friends.

I put my hand on her shoulder. 'Wake up!' I said loudly.

Vicks opened her eyes. They rested on me, and I saw something in them. Something that hadn't been there before. Like some-one had staked her.

Oh fuck. I've killed her!

'Um...I have to help you eat,' I said, unsurely, because I didn't know who that was staring at me like that. She had *never* stared at me like that. Like I was her murderer.

Victoria pushed the tray off the bedside table. It fell onto the floor, the soup splashing on the carpet. She stared at me, her eyes bristling with anger.

Frig! All that politeness had gone. She had a face like a toilet mess, all the shit showing. What the fuck?

'Get out,' she said in a low, growling voice, '*Get out.*'

'O.K. I get it. *I get it.* You didn't like it. I won't ever take you to another rally again. You can be your stuffy old self ... I want you to be, because *frig,* I don't know who that is lookin' out your face...'

Vicks picked up a book on her tableside. She threw it hard at me and the corner of the book struck my face.

'Get OUT!'

Fuck! I thought, getting out of the room, and shutting the door fast, before she threw something else at me. Maybe Vicks had some brain damage?

'Mum?' I called out. 'Can you call the Doctor and get him to do another home visit? Something's wrong. I think...I think...' tears fell from my eyes and my voice wobbled, 'I think she's got a bit of brain damage, maybe because she hit her head too hard?'

My mother turned and looked at me coldly, picking up the phone. 'See what happens when you take people out of their natural flight path?'

'She wasn't that much in flight...really...' I hiccupped.

'If Victoria has brain damage, I will never, *never* forgive you,' my mother said to me, her face vicious.

'Um...'

I turned and fled into my room.

I shut the door of my room, leaning against the door, trying not to crack. I couldn't stop my legs shaking or my thoughts on hotwires. I looked at my unmade bed, the scores of music sheets littered around on the floor, the ashtray with stubbed out cigarettes and all the feminist literature and posters I had; all seemed to jumble together into a BIG mess. Crying, I opened the window. I grabbed the ashtray and threw it out the window. I ripped up every poster, flier and article on changing women and threw it out as well. I straightened out the sheets on my bed. I gathered up all my music notes and held them close to my chest. I closed my eyes, rocking from side to side. *This was all I had left, this was natural, this was natural, this was me, this was me...*

This is me.

P. C. VERRONE

What to Watch

This is the one where she gets the guy. This is the one where she doesn't get the guy but realizes her best friend's been in love with her all along. This is the one where she could get the guy, but instead she tells him off and gets drinks with her new rag-tag gang. This is the one where she's in the cab but jumps out and runs to him and they kiss in the rain. This is the one where she's in the cab and stays seated and gets to the airport and she never sees him again but you know that she thinks about him every time that Arctic Monkeys song plays. This is the one where she's in the cab and she thinks she'll never see him again but then the cab driver turns around and it's HIM and there are no airports or Arctic Monkeys. This is the one where she plays a lesbian who dies. She won an Oscar for that. This is the one where she plays a victim of domestic abuse, which sparked some speculation around her divorce from her second husband. She should've won an Oscar for that. This is the one everyone says is her best – better than the Oscar one or the robbed-of-an-Oscar one. Everyone has their reasons, but I think it's this one moment – so fast you could miss it – when her eyes catch the camera and she smiles, like she knows you're watching, and she's watching too.

MIRANDA OVERETT

Pineapples

It was only after having children, and what happened next, that she discovered her love of minor dishonesties. *I bet you didn't know that giraffes can breathe underwater,* she told them as they walked the slow path to the park, and they wide-eyed-and-shocked at her, and she nodded impressive, grown-up knowledge right back. *Now, remember – only cross at the traffic lights.*

Be kind to each other, she said later, pouring warm water over their soft limbs, *and – when bees get tired, they fly upside down.*

The next day, she spent the morning teaching them to break eggs and strip away tired potato skins, and told them, *tiny dinosaurs, too small to see, live in the cracks in the pavement.* Over lunch, she explained that, unlike dinosaurs, humans do not last forever.

Tuesdays are a few seconds shorter than all the other days, she told them that evening, leaning, conspiratorial, across their small beds, breathing them in, *so you have to make the most of them. And remembering takes practice – try and think of the things you love every day.*

A few weeks later, lying flat and intubated, she held their small hands and told them, *I'm not going anywhere, I promise. And pineapples? They grow underground.*

ANGELA WIPPERMAN

The Value of Things

A small, black glove. A fit for slender fingers; leather with its gravelly shine. It was lying flat beneath a branch in the undergrowth just off the gravel path, the fingers outstretched as if reaching.

Earlier:

A rush in the night, a packing of things, but what to take. The rings in the jewellery box? The can of beans? The big scarf (*what if it gets cold? But it takes up so much room*). The value of things has become confused: where they are going, beans may be more valuable than rings. And yet ... gold always has that allure. They make piles of what to take, what to hide, what to leave. The value of people, too, is altered (*the staff are asleep upstairs*).

Soft, unmarked hands wrap porcelain in silk and shove it down at the bottom of the wardrobe (*perhaps it won't be found in there*). Forget the good shoes, boots are the thing for walking. And thick socks. Roll cotton up tight and pack it down into the cases (*sew the rings into the lining*).

The leather gloves are the last things she takes. They lie like bat wings over the back of the Sheraton. Leather is good for warmth, and these are wool lined. She slips them on, the last thing she does in that house before they leave.

ANDREW BOULTON

Swim the Bay with Byron
(only 14 Euros)

At Nacché there's a man who dresses as Byron and will swim with you across the bay. Actually, Byron never swam this bay, not that we know of. He'd certainly swam the bay at Portovenere, but my Byron was chased away from there for bothering tourists. It made me itchy, looking at my Byron, like when you see a red mite wander across somebody else's skin. But I paid my fourteen euros and left my bag with a pale boy dressed as Shelley. I joked that, by the looks of him, this Shelley must be the one who drowned not far from here, but my face must have seemed sad when I said it because they only looked sorry. A quarter of a mile across the bay my Byron stopped to tread water. This, I gather, was the depth at which his seductions either felt most charming or least threatening. I negotiated us into small talk instead of a mid-sea fumble, although he did tell me his foreskin reacted so furiously these days to the salt he'd tried to limit how much actual sex he had in the sea. I nodded, sympathetically, and asked if he could recite some Childe Harold for me, here in this bay that Byron probably never saw. My Byron bobbed and blushed and, after a while, I began swimming back, noticing then that dead Shelley was nowhere to be seen, and feeling thankful that, at last, we'd welcomed a little poetry into the day.

Unsent

After my father died, during those long, languid days we spent unburdening our childhood home of once-loved belongings, I found a letter in the drawer of his desk.

In it, my father wrote to a man I'd never met, telling him he was in love with him. He'd felt that way since 1967, when they'd met aged seventeen – two years before mum – when their parents had rented neighbouring caravans near Barmouth beach for the same fortnight.

I thought back to holidays on that same beach in my youth, before we upgraded to Alicante and a timeshare with a pool; days spent enveloped by a polyester windbreaker, eating picnics of pork pies, Smiths crisps with blue salt sachets, cubed cheese, and radishes straight out of the bag.

My father, building us sandcastles, was always a little distant; no more or less than usual, but strangely not present – and whenever the waves washed away his work, he'd just shrug his shoulders or start again.

'Dad, I've got something to tell you,' I'd said to him two decades later. Mum was gone by then. We were in a pub after the match, just us. Everyone else already knew, of course.

'That's good,' he'd said. 'I'm dead chuffed for you. Lads couldn't be so open in my day.'

Such a normal thing to say, I'd thought nothing of it. But in that old, emptying house, his letter in my hands, so much suddenly made sense, while so much was left unsaid.

CHARLOTTE MORBEY

Trauma Light

We're both blue under this light. Colour splashes down the line of emergency vehicles, a soundless disco of strobing white headlights. Watchers drift by, phones clamped to their intact windows. A brief audience for your latest disaster. There's the twisted graveyard that was your Audi. That burning heap was a transit van and the central barrier.

This was your fault.

You won't be able to charm your way out of this one. I watch realisation dawning on your face, in the widening of your eyes, your bottom lip vanishing between expensive teeth. I meant it when I said I wouldn't make it alright any more. Not even this, the absolutely-the-last, promise-no-more-times time.

The paramedic squeezed your shoulder before swinging down the steps. 'We'll go. Leave the trauma light on,' he says. So now it's only us. Me lying and you talking, our acknowledged rule of engagement. Your sarcasm via shouting to threats. My silent resentment.

I wait while you try for the right words. If you say sorry now you are doing better than I will. I stare back, unspeaking, my face blank and cold as a hospital tile. I never saw you cry before. You look younger. If the static lump that was my heart could melt, perhaps it would.

Instead, we stuck in our lanes until you didn't. Now we're both under this blue light, your skin shifting into sweaty goosebumps while I set like cold marble.

MARY MORRISSY

Present Perfect

When she had pulled open the garage door that night, she was primed for a domestic mishap. A minor fall, his phone left off the hook. Her father didn't own a mobile. He was old school, a short-sighted reader, a crossword fanatic, a stickler for grammar. Couldn't abide a split infinitive; railed against semi-colon abuse. As for the present perfect …

Rules are rules for a reason, he used to say, and don't annoy me with the common usage defence.

She didn't.

Even with the door open, she couldn't see far into the gloom. There was no moon and she didn't have a torch. It wasn't until she'd made her way gingerly inside, feeling her way amongst the looming silhouettes of packing cases and abandoned furniture that alarm set in. Underfoot, she crushed something flimsy that sounded like the cracking of a tiny bone. When she bent down to feel on the ground her fingers met the skewed arm of his glasses and a shattered lens.

She stood up, still blind in the furry darkness, and the flocky nap of his sock kissed her lips. Why do people always abandon their shoes for this, as if they were entering a sacred space or a house with a parquet floor?

And then his voice came to her – 'paintings are hung; people are hanged'.

SHELLEY ROCHE-JACQUES

New You

When the woman collapses on the platform they somehow assume you're her friend. The paramedics hand you her gorgeous camel coat and ask if you can get the baby home safely. The woman is still unconscious as they stretcher her off towards the platform lifts.

It's easier just to slip the coat on. A man with nice hair appears and heaves the expensive baby buggy onto the train. You thank him with new-found grace.

In the Buggy Zone you don't pull down a seat. You like the swing of the coat too much. You put a hand into one of the pockets and let your fingers roam. A couple of pound coins enmeshed in shredded tissue and an old train ticket. You will take better care.

A woman squeezing past peers into the buggy. 'Beautiful', she murmurs. You smile a timeless sort of smile and rearrange the covers with your best motherly concern. You take a look for yourself. The sleeping baby is mole-like. A curved little paw pokes out of the blanket. You wonder if it's a boy or a girl. Everything is so tastefully neutral. A string of yellow cotton elephants dance hypnotically to the rhythm of the train.

As you plunge into a tunnel the lights make everything drained and artificial. You close your eyes, smooth your coat, edge gently away from the buggy. You will skip off at the next stop, chic and unencumbered, ready to live your best life.

Biographies

Judges' Biographies

Raymond Antrobus was born in London, Hackney to an English mother and Jamaican father, he is the author of *Shapes & Disfigurements*, *To Sweeten Bitter*, *The Perseverance* and *All The Names Given*. In 2019 he became the first ever poet to be awarded the Rathbone Folio Prize for best work of literature in any genre.

Other accolades include the Ted Hughes award, PBS Winter Choice, A Sunday Times Young Writer of the year award & The Guardian Poetry Book Of The Year 2018, as well as a shortlist for the Griffin Prize and Forward Prize. In 2018 he was awarded 'The Geoffrey Dearmer Prize', (Judged by Ocean Vuong), for his poem 'Sound Machine'. Also in 2019, his poem 'Jamaican British' was added to the GCSE syllabus. He is the recipient of fellowships from Cave Canem, Complete Works 3 and Jerwood Compton. He is also one of the world's first recipients of an MA in Spoken Word education from Goldsmiths University. Raymond is a founding member of 'Chill Pill' and 'Keats House Poets Forum' and is an Ambassador for 'The Poetry School'. His poems have been published in *POETRY*, *Poetry Review*, *New Statesman*, *The Deaf Poets Society*, as well as in anthologies from Bloodaxe, Peepal Tree Press and Nine Arches. Raymond has read and performed his poetry at festivals (Glastonbury, Latitude, BOCAS etc) to universities (Oxford, Goldsmiths, Warwick etc). He has won numerous Slams (Farrago International Slam Champion 2010, The Canterbury Slam 2013 and was joint winner at the Open Calabash Slam in 2016).

His poetry has appeared on BBC 2, BBC Radio 4, *The Big Issue*, *The Jamaica Gleaner*, *The Guardian* and at TedxEastEnd.

Robert McCrum, who was born and educated in Cambridge, is a writer and editor whose book, *Every Third Thought: On Life, Death and the Endgame*, was published to great acclaim in 2017, when it was also serialised on BBC Radio 4.

From 1980 to 1996, McCrum was editor-in-chief of Faber & Faber, where he published Kazuo Ishiguro, Harold Pinter, Milan Kundera, Peter Carey, Danilo Kis, Paul Auster, Marilynne Robinson, Lorrie Moore, Adam Phillips, Mario Vargas Llosa, Jayne Anne Phillips, Orhan Pamuk, Adam Mars-Jones, and Hanif Kureishi among many others. At the same time, he wrote six novels, and co-authored the BBC TV series, *The Story of English*, for which he was awarded an Emmy, and the Peabody Prize in 1987.

In July 1995, McCrum suffered a serious stroke, a personal crisis he described in *My Year Off*, a book now regarded as an essential study in the understanding of the condition.

He was Literary Editor of the *Observer* from 1996 to 2010, and published his award-winning biography *P.G. Wodehouse: A Life* in 2004. *Globish* (2010) was an international bestseller. *My Year Off* (1998), is now in its third edition as a Picador Classic.

McCrum was appointed Associate Editor of the *Observer* in 2008. He left the Guardian Media Group in January 2018 to pursue his own literary interests. His latest book *Shakespearean: On Life and Language in Times of Disruption* was published in September 2020 by Picador/Macmillan.

Writers' biographies

Cait Atherton was born on the myth-drenched Isle of Man. Her childhood rained with stories of folklore and family. A drier adult life in Cambridge as a medical scientist came to an end with a posting to Thailand, the rain became a monsoon immersing her in Eastern philosophy with voyages to India, Nepal, Tibet. Along the way she realised that she'd like to pour her own small offering into to the great ocean of words. Much failure and some success. It's not the winning, it's knowing that an offering has been accepted. Thank you Bridport.

Andrew Boulton is a lecturer in creative advertising and creative writing at the University of Lincoln. He is the author of a bestselling book on copywriting and a children's book called *Adele Writes an Ad*. His stories have been accepted and published in journals including *Retreat West*, *Lunate Fiction*, *Flash Fiction Magazine*, *Tiny Molecules*, *Spelk*, *Reflex*, *Bath Flash Fiction* anthology, *Cranked Anvil* and *Storgy*. He lives in Nottingham with his wife, daughter and a chubby cat. Find him on Twitter: @boultini

Matt Buttell-Rogers is a writer and copy editor from north London, where he lives with his husband. He studied Creative Studies in English at Bath Spa University and has been working as a copywriter and editor across various sectors and industries since graduating in 2006. His main passions are reading, writing, and playing board games; he runs his own book club and owns over 120 tabletop games. He has previously written for *Gay Times*, the *Guardian*, Zatu Games, Ticketmaster and Sky. He is currently working on his first novel.

Jennie Ziverk Carr is a native daughter of the Ozark Mountains in Missouri, USA. Writing has been an important expressive outlet through every stage of her life – as a child, an art historian, a teacher, and currently, as a homeschooling mother-of-two in Texas. Jennie has developed her writing portfolio over many years, and is proud to begin submitting her work for competition and publication. Her writing has been featured in NPR's 2018 Poetry Month series and on Rhode Island Public Radio's program This I Believe: New England. Jennie is eager to pursue more opportunities to share and to publish her work.

Courtney Conrad is a Jamaican poet. Her poetry explores the intersectional politics of race, religion, gender, sexuality and migration. She is a current member of Malika's Poetry Kitchen and the London Library Emerging Writers Programme. She is an alumna of the Roundhouse Poetry Collective. Her poems have appeared in *The White Review*, *Magma Poetry*, *Poetry Birmingham Literary Journal*, *Stand Magazine*, and *Poetry Wales* and anthologised by Bad Betty Press and Anamot Press. She was shortlisted for The White Review Poet's Prize 2020 and longlisted for the Rebecca Swift Women Poets' Prize 2020 and The Rialto Nature and Place Poetry Competition.

Gemma Cooper-Novack's debut poetry collection *We Might As Well Be Underwater* (Unsolicited Press, 2017) was a finalist for the Central New York Book Award. She's published chapbooks with Warren Tales (*Too Much Like a Landscape*) and The Head & the Hand (*Bedside Manner*). Her poetry and fiction have appeared in more than forty journals; her plays have been produced across the United States. She is a 2016 Deming Fund grantee and a doctoral candidate in literacy education at Syracuse University. Her website is www.gemmacoopernovack.com

Jo Davis' poetry has appeared in magazines such as *PN Review*, *Strix*, *Ink Sweat & Tears*, *Butcher's Dog*, anthologies *Alter Egos* (Bad Betty Press) and *Cry of the Poor* (Culture Matters), and is currently longlisted for the Winchester Prize. She was guest editor of *Tentacular* and a poetry editor for *The Mays*. She ran Darwin College Poetry Society at the University of Cambridge, where she completed her PhD and won the William Barclay Squire Essay Prize. She founded writers' group Coppermill Poets, whose book-length poem, *The Patchwork Epic of Waltham Forest*, was commissioned for Words Over Waltham Forest literary festival.

Armen Davoudian is the author of *Swan Song*, which won the 2020 Frost Place Chapbook Competition. His poems and translations from Persian appear in *AGNI*, *The Sewanee Review*, *The Yale Review*, and elsewhere. He grew up in Isfahan, Iran and lives in California, where he is a PhD candidate in English at Stanford University.

Alana Franasiak is a writer based in Portland, Maine. She graduated from Lesley University with an MFA in Fiction. Her stories have been selected as a semi-finalist in The Raymond Carver Short Story Contest and as a finalist in The Salamander Fiction Contest. She is currently working on two novels.

Stephanie Early Green's short fiction appears or is forthcoming in *Narrative Magazine*, *The Chicago Tribune*, *New Ohio Review*, *Juked*, and elsewhere. Her work was selected by Rumaan Alam as a finalist in the 2021 Crazyhorse Fiction Prize, and she has been named a finalist in the 2021 Montana Prize for Fiction, the 2020 Halifax Ranch Fiction Prize, and others. She has been named a 2021 Fellow at the Virginia Center for Creative Arts and has participated in Bread Loaf, Community of Writers, Kenyon Review, and One Story writing conferences. She is at work on a novel. Her website is https://stephanieearlygreen.com/.

Susannah Hart's debut collection *Out of True* won the Live Canon First Collection Prize in 2018 and her poem *Reading the Safeguarding and Child Protection Policy* won first prize in the 2020 National Poetry Competition. She has been widely published in magazines and online. Susannah is on the board of Magma Poetry, works as a freelance copywriter and is a long-serving governor at her local primary school.

Erin Lambert Hartman is an American poet and the author of the chapbook *Resolution* (Finishing Line Press, 2008). Her poetry has appeared in journals such as *Blackbird*, *Colorado Review*, *DIAGRAM*, and *The Madison Review*. This Bridport Anthology is her first international publication. She earned an MFA in creative writing from Syracuse University (2001), and has taught at Hostos Community College, Virginia Commonwealth University, and James Madison University. Erin is now a licensed massage therapist and owns a small healing arts practice in Harrisonburg, Virginia.

Lois P. Jones' awards include the Bristol Poetry Prize judged by Liz Berry, the Lascaux Poetry Prize, the Tiferet Poetry Prize and as winning finalist for the 2018 Terrain Poetry Contest judged by Jane Hirshfield. Jones has work published or forthcoming in *Plume, Guernica Editions 2021, New Voices: Contemporary Writers Confronting the Holocaust* (Vallentine Mitchell of London – 2021*); Publishers Weekly, Arabic Edition "Al-Nasher Al-Usboei"; Verse Daily,* and *Narrative.* Jones' first collection, *Night Ladder* was published by Glass Lyre Press and listed for several awards. She is the poetry editor for *Kyoto Journal* and a screening judge for the Kingsley-Tufts Awards.

Nick Makoha is the founder of The Obsidian Foundation. Winner of the 2021 Ivan Juritz prize. In 2017, Nick's debut collection, *Kingdom of Gravity*, was shortlisted for the Felix Dennis Prize for Best First Collection and was one of the *Guardian*'s best books of the year. Nick is a Cave Canem Graduate Fellow and the Complete Works alumnus. He won the 2015 Brunel International African Poetry Prize and the 2016 Toi Derricotte & Cornelius Eady Prize. His poems have appeared in the *Cambridge Review*, the *New York Times, Poetry Review, Rialto, Poetry London, TriQuarterly Review, Boston Review, Callaloo* and *Wasafiri.*

Charlin McIsaac is an actor, singer, writer, and general all-around funny gal based in Toronto. She has collaborated on a number of devised theatre projects and has featured in several award-winning plays and is now branching into prose writing. *Manischewitz Night* is her first publication. Charlin is interested in stories about women who are mischievous and gross and playful and complicated and irreverent. You can find her on Twitter @charlinmcisaac.

Charlotte Morbey lives on a hill in rural Scotland, with her husband and two of her three children. As a community midwife she feels lucky to work with remote communities in an inspirational landscape. Having moved around southern England before relocating to Scotland, she couldn't tell you where she is from these days. She has come back to writing in midlife after chronic illness and a change of career. Charlotte is currently editing a novel, set in the Highlands in 1923. 'Trauma Light' is her first published flash fiction. Find her on Twitter: @charmotwit

Mary Morrissy is the author of three novels, *Mother of Pearl, The Pretender* and *The Rising of Bella Casey*, two collections of stories, *A Lazy Eye*, and *Prosperity Drive* and is a recent convert to flash. Her work has won the Hennessy Prize (for short fiction) and a Lannan Foundation Award and has been twice nominated for the Dublin International Literary

Award and shortlisted for the Whitbread Prize (now Costa). She is a journalist and teacher of creative writing and offers literary mentoring. Her website can be found at https://marymorrissy.com

Eileen O'Donoghue is a fiction writer living in south-west Ireland. Her short fiction has been shortlisted for the Fish short story prize in 2018, longlisted for the Fabula Press short story contest in 2017, and highly commended in the Michael Terence short story competition in 2021. Her stories have been published in *The Quarryman*, the literary journal of University College Cork in 2017, 2018 and 2021. She has an MA from UCC and has just submitted her thesis for an MA in Creative Writing at the University of Limerick. She is currently working on her first novel. Twitter: @Eilertweets1

Miranda Overett is a writer of odd experiences – from teaching toddlers in Thailand, to making schedules for film shoots in London, and dabbling in stand-up comedy in Budapest. Today, she still lives in her adopted home of Hungary, and has had articles, poetry and flash fiction published in the *Huffington Post*, the *Masters Review*, *Sad Girls Club*, *Paragraph Planet*, and more. She has recently completed an MA in Creative Writing, and is currently working on her first novel.

Dhyanna Raffi-David lives in a Southern California with her three children, a vegetable garden, and a *shimmer* of hummingbirds. She received her MFA in creative writing from the Iowa Writers Workshop and is currently working on a short story collection.

Stevie Reeves is the trumpet playing editor of a literary magazine. She writes and lives in Surrey with her husband, son and a deaf French bulldog. She has lived and studied in the USA and identifies herself as transatlantic. She studied English Literature and Language at Oxford University and is currently working on the Creative Writing Programme with New Writing South. Stevie also writes poetry and her poems have been published and listed for awards by Shoreham Wordfest, Mslexia Women's Poetry Competition and Prole Pamphlet Competition. She is currently finishing her novel and working on a collection of short stories.

Shelley Roche-Jacques' work has appeared in magazines such as *Litro, Magma, The Rialto*, and *The Boston Review*. Her poetry pamphlet *Ripening Dark* was published in 2015, followed by a collection of dramatic monologues, *Risk the Pier*, in 2017. She is interested in the idea of balancing 'sympathy and judgement' in her stories and monologues, of coming at political ideas obliquely, and in creating characters with whom the reader might not feel entirely comfortable. She lives in Barnsley, Yorkshire, and lectures in Creative Writing at Sheffield Hallam University.

T.C. Smith received his MFA from the University of Washington. A sixth generation Texan, he now makes his home in the Pacific Northwest. In 2019, an excerpt from his novel, *No Man's Land*, was longlisted for the Stockholm First Pages Prize. 'Minotaur', from the same novel, is forthcoming in Gargoyle Literary Magazine. The Bridport Prize marks his fiction debut. Other interests include film (M.A., University of Southern California), Scandinavian Languages and Literature (M.A., University of Washington), hiking in the Cascade Mountains, and reading (classic narrative fiction, autobiography, film/world history 1900-1929). He currently works for the University of Washington Libraries.

Greta Stoddart's first book of poems *At Home in the Dark* (Anvil) was shortlisted for the Forward Prize for Best First Collection and won the Geoffrey Faber Memorial Prize in 2002. Her second, *Salvation Jane* (Anvil), was shortlisted for the Costa Book Award 2008 and third, *Alive Alive O* (Bloodaxe, 2015), was shortlisted for the Roehampton Prize 2016 with a poem shortlisted for the Forward Prize for Best Individual Poem. Her latest work, *Who's there?*, broadcast on Radio 4 was BBC Pick of the Week and shortlisted for the 2017 Ted Hughes Award. Her new book *Fool* will be published by Bloodaxe in 2022. *The Leavetaking* is her first published short story. She lives in Devon and teaches for the Poetry School.

Hannah Sutherland is a writer from the North-East of Scotland. Her debut novel, *Life Lessons,* was longlisted in Helen Lederer's Comedy Women in Print Award 2021 in the unpublished category. She placed 2nd in the Writing East Midland's Aurora Awards 2020 and won Cranked Anvil's Flash Fiction Prize. Her Novella-in-Flash, *Small Things,* placed Highly Commended in the Bath Novella-in-Flash Award 2021 and will be published later in the year by Ad Hoc Fiction. She's a selective Curtis Brown Creative alumina and is studying for her MFA in Creative Writing at the Manchester Writing School. She tweets at @HannahWrites88.

David Swann's stories and poems have now won nine awards at The Bridport Prize. His book *The Privilege of Rain* (Waterloo Press, 2010), about his residency in a high-security prison, was shortlisted for The Ted Hughes Award. He teaches at The University of Chichester, and is the author of a forthcoming novella, *Season of Bright Sorrow* (Ad Hoc, 2021). Dave started his working life as a reporter on Accrington Stanley's football matches and has now recovered from the excitement. He divides his time between Brighton and Hove.

Jane Thomas is a British poet based in Oxford. She is currently completing a pamphlet on the subject of Alzheimer's. In 20/21 she has been shortlisted in The Rialto Pamphlet Competition, The PS Stanza, Fish, Live Canon, Poetry Wales and The FPM-Hippocrates Prize and published in: *Stand*, *The Rialto*, *Envoi*, *Mslexia* and *The Oakland Review*. Her work has been included in anthologies including NAHR, Ver Poets, Hippocrates, Live Canon and Glean & Graft. She is an active member of Oxford Stanza II and Ver Poets and occasional reviewer for *Sphinx*. https://www.janethomas.org/ @janethomas33

Kathy Tierney is a writer who lives in Australia and has poetry and creative non-fiction published in various journals. She has won three poetry awards; The 2004 Newcastle Poetry Prize-local (joint first prize), The 2005 Dennis Butler Memorial Award: Free Form Poetry (1st prize) and the Bessie Jennings Award Literary Writing Competition 2017 (2nd prize). She has also won a commended award for a short story in the 2007 Roland Robinson Literary Award. She has an Associate Degree of Creative Writing from Southern Cross University, and a Bachelor of Creative Writing with Distinction from Deakin University, Australia.

Jessica Traynor's debut collection, *Liffey Swim* (Dedalus Press, 2014), was shortlisted for the Strong/Shine Award and in 2016 was named one of the best poetry debuts of the past five years on Bustle.com. *The Quick*, was a 2019 *Irish Times* poetry choice. Awards include the Ireland Chair of Poetry Bursary and Hennessy New Writer of the Year. *Paper Boat,* a new opera commission, will premiere in 2022. Residencies in 2021-22 include Yeats Society Sligo, The Seamus Heaney Home Place and the DLR LexIcon. She is a Creative Fellow of UCD. *Pit Lullabies* will be published by Bloodaxe Books in 2022.

P.C. Verrone is a writer, theatrical artist, and storyteller born and raised in Los Angeles, California. His plays have been presented by the Blank

Theater, Center Theatre Group, Custom Made Theater, and Native Voices. He was awarded a 2021-22 Many Voices Fellowship at the Playwrights' Center in Minneapolis, Minnesota. He is a participant in the inaugural Black Creatives Revision Workshop, a collaboration between We Need Diverse Books and Penguin Random House. He graduated from Harvard University. He is currently working on a theatrical commission from the Urbanite Theater as well as his debut novel.

Emma Walton Hamilton is an author, editor, producer, and arts educator. She has written or co-written over thirty books for children and young adults, as well as two memoirs and a book on raising readers. A faculty member of Stony Brook University's MFA in Creative Writing and Literature, she teaches children's literature and playwriting. Her poems have been published in *SCBWI's Bulletin, Julie Andrews' Collection of Poems, Songs and Lullabies* and *Treasury For All Seasons*, and the Texas Education Agency's "Assessment of Academic Readiness, Grade 5," among others. She holds a masters degree in Creative Writing from Stony Brook.

Adam Welch is a creative copywriter and editor based in London, where he works in the fashion industry. His fiction has appeared in *Ambit, Open Pen, Short Fiction, Shooter* and Salt's *Best British Short Stories 2019*. He was highly commended in the 2020 University of Essex / Short Fiction Prize, longlisted in the 2018 London Short Story Prize and one of three Arvon/Jerwood fiction mentees for 2019/20. He's currently working on a collection of short stories set in and around commercial and hyper-capitalist spaces alongside his first novel and a number of screenwriting projects. His website is http://www.adamwelchwriter.com

Adrienne Wilkinson's debut pamphlet, *repeating mouths*, in which 'both the lesbian erotic and the traumatic body are explored under a lens of curiosity', was published by Broken Sleep Books in August 2021. Her poems have appeared in *The Interpreter's House, bath magg*, and *The Manchester Review*, and her poetry features in an upcoming anthology on deviance from Toothgrinder Press. Her critical writing appeared in photography book *Tilt*, published by First Light. Adrienne is poetry editor at *Asylum*, a radical mental health magazine that platforms a variety of voices. She works in a plant shop and studies MA Poetry at the University of East Anglia.

Angela Wipperman grew up in Essex and now lives and works in London. She has published short fiction in Litro and elsewhere, has been shortlisted for the Retreat West First Chapters competition, and is working on her first novel. She is an alumnus of the 2020 Faber Academy novel writing course. Outside of her fiction writing she is a science writer and communicator.